The twentieth century has seen biology come of age as a conceptual and quantitative science. Major functional phenomena rather than catalogues of animals and plants comprise the core of MODERN BIOLOGY; such heretofore seemingly unrelated fields as cytology, biochemistry, and genetics are now being unified into a common framework at the molecular level.

The purpose of this Series is to introduce the beginning student in college biology—as well as the gifted high school student and all interested readers—both to the concepts unifying the fields of biology and to the diversity of facts that give the entire field its unique texture. Each book in the Series is an introduction to one of the major foundation stones in the mosaic. Taken together, they provide an integration of the general and the comparative, the cellular and the organismic, the animal and the plant, the structural and the functional—in sum, a solid overview of the dynamic science that is MODERN BIOLOGY.

MODERN BIOLOGY SERIES

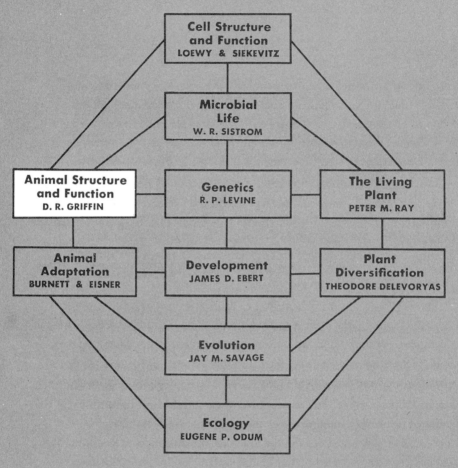

Cell Structure and Function — LOEWY & SIEKEVITZ

Microbial Life — W. R. SISTROM

Animal Structure and Function — D. R. GRIFFIN

Genetics — R. P. LEVINE

The Living Plant — PETER M. RAY

Animal Adaptation — BURNETT & EISNER

Development — JAMES D. EBERT

Plant Diversification — THEODORE DELEVORYAS

Evolution — JAY M. SAVAGE

Ecology — EUGENE P. ODUM

HOLT, RINEHART AND WINSTON

NEW YORK · CHICAGO · SAN FRANCISCO · TORONTO · LONDON

ANIMAL

STRUCTURE

AND

FUNCTION

DONALD R. GRIFFIN

HARVARD UNIVERSITY

Cover photograph, *Globigerina*, courtesy of
the American Museum of Natural History

PREFACE

This book is dedicated to the importance of understanding living animals. Its emphasis is on principles of organization rather than on the variety of animals or their lines of descent. In this era of technological accomplishments it is easy to focus too much of our attention on artificial devices and the large-scale operations they make possible. Petroleum refineries and intercontinental rockets impress us by their size, power, and complexity, while at first glance the body of an animal seems soft and ineffective. Yet only very little investigation is needed to reveal that the organs of any animal carry out far more complicated operations than the most intricate machine. If we overlook this fact, we fall into the absurd error of thinking about living protoplasm, including that which makes up our own bodies, as though it really *were* nothing but an odorous jelly. Certainly when killed it is little more, but in its natural state of life and activity almost any part of any animal is performing a number of difficult operations simultaneously. Through its precise control and balance of these many processes protoplasm has managed to reshape the world.

It is vitally important that all students of science at the college level should appreciate the structure and functioning of the most successful mechanisms of which we have any knowledge, the organ systems of living animals. In order to pass beyond the descriptive level, it will be assumed that readers of this book have an elementary knowledge of physics and chemistry. Biology has often been presented to the college student as though he had just stepped innocently out of the eighteenth century without having met such terms as diffusion, ion, molecule, oxygen, or voltage. But for many years our high schools, and even junior high schools, have been presenting sufficient material from the physical sciences to allow anything in this book to be understood without undue effort. It is now appropriate to assume that students have not been wasting their time while studying science before entering college. The college students of this generation have matured more rapidly than their parents (or their teachers), and they deserve a mature and straightforward presentation of any subject they are asked to study.

Many traditional aspects of zoology are absent from the following pages, or severely condensed, but the most significant of them are covered in other books of this series. The science of biology is evolving, or at least undergoing metamorphosis. Fundamental material missing from chapter titles will often be found in new contexts where it can more appropriately be related to other active areas of science. For example, the comparative anatomy of the heart and circulatory system is treated, not as evidence for the evolution of mammals from fishes and amphibians, but as one aspect of a functional system, adapted differently in the various classes of vertebrates for the same basic needs. If physiology seems to receive more emphasis than morphology, it is because of the author's belief that when both are clearly understood the distinction between them ceases to be important. The aim throughout has been to present zoology in the true sense—with the animals, not mechanisms or molecules, at the center of the stage.

I wish to thank the authors and publishers who granted permission to reproduce the photomicrographs for Figures 3-4, 10-5, and 10-7. It is a special pleasure to express my grateful appreciation to Helen E. Speiden for her patient, skillful, and thoughtful work in producing the original drawings for the remaining illustrations.

D.R.G.

Cambridge, Massachusetts
June, 1962

CONTENTS

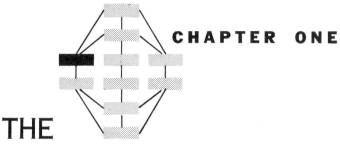

CHAPTER ONE

THE SIGNIFICANCE OF ANIMALS IN MODERN SCIENCE

INTRODUCTION—Out of the whole universe nothing we know or even seriously imagine can compare with the intricate machinery that makes up living animals. The physical sciences restrict their scope to systems lending themselves to simple explanations. The proper study of animals and plants, however, calls for a higher order of analysis and understanding. Biology is intrinsically more difficult than physics and chemistry and has a closer importance for us, because our own bodies and our ways of life are largely conditioned by its orderly complexities.

Intelligent men have long recognized that animals are our distant relatives. A century ago this was a radical doctrine that generated an emotional cyclone about the heads of Darwin and his fellow thinkers when they called for a readjustment of basic beliefs about our relationship to the rest of the universe. No other idea since the Copernican revolution has so profoundly altered human thinking as the biological concept of evolution. This subject is considered in another book of this series (*Evolution*), and we will take it for granted here that animals and men are descended from different, usually simpler, animals that lived millions of years ago, and furthermore that some of these lines of descent can be traced back through the fossil record.

One striking attribute of animals is their diversity, and the patient labors of several generations of biologists have left us with an embarrassment of factual riches about the million-odd forms of animal life with which we share this earth. Each has been given a name, and every part of any given sort of animal has also been identified so that one biologist may know what another is talking about. Although this stockpile of information about animals may stagger the imagination, it also tends to stun the intellect. Fortunately, however, many new, important, and exciting facts have recently been learned about the efficient design of animal bodies and the manner in which their many parts work together in functional harmony.

CELLS, MICROBES, PLANTS, AND ANIMALS

Close examination of any animal shows that it is built up from microscopic units of organized life called *cells*. These are usually a few microns in length or width (one micron, or μ, $= 10^{-4}$ centimeter or $1/25000$ inch) and are surrounded by *cell membranes* so thin that they can only barely be seen under the best microscopes employing visible light. So many of the basic phenomena of life occur in the viscous, jellylike material called *protoplasm* that is bounded by cell membranes that one book of this series (*Cell Structure and Function*) is devoted wholly to the fundamental processes that occur within the confines of single cells. Many living organisms consist of only one cell, and these are usually known as microbes. But those we ordinarily call animals are composed of thousands, or more often millions, of cells specialized into dozens or hundreds of distinct types. Very few of these cells are capable of living independently outside the organized body of which they form a part. Yet when functioning together they add up to an animal that does things no population of microbes could ever hope to match.

Plants, of course, are also multicellular living organisms, and they are distinguished from animals, in general, by lack of movement and by the ability to synthesize food materials from simple molecules by trapping the energy of sunlight in the process of *photosynthesis*. Plants and microbes that can carry out photosynthesis are called *autotrophic* in contrast to the typical animal, which is designated *heterotrophic* because it must obtain the energy it needs by consuming as food molecules that have been synthesized by plants or other living organisms. There are notable exceptions to this general rule. Many animals live most of their life in a very inactive state, often attached to the bottom of the ocean; examples are clams and oysters, or the corals, which secrete around their bodies hard protective shells that pile up by the millions to form the rock of coral reefs. Flowers may open and close their petals every day, and many of the microscopic aquatic plants called *algae* swim actively at some stage in their lives. Furthermore, there are plants such as the fungi, which are incapable of photosynthesis and are quite as heterotrophic as a codfish or a cow. On the other hand, certain corals and related animals have intimate associations with single-celled algae. The algal cells are scattered among those of the coral and carry out photosynthesis for the mutual benefit of themselves and the surrounding animal so that the combination becomes an autotrophic entity.

Among microbes the distinction between animallike, heterotrophic cells and plantlike, autotrophic ones becomes even more difficult to follow. In some cases the very same cell changes during its lifetime from a form that is autotrophic and motionless to one that swims actively and carries out no photosynthesis; or, it may be both mobile and autotrophic at the same time. When biology was dominated by the effort to classify living organisms, zoologists who studied animals claimed the more mobile microbes as members of the Animal Kingdom while botanists classified the photosynthetic ones as plants. This led to some entertaining jurisdictional disputes when the same microbe changed its way of life. Modern biologists, however, place much more emphasis on the distinction between microbes and multicellular organisms, because so many significant processes are regulated at cell membranes or occur within single cells. Quite different phenomena present themselves when we consider how large numbers of cells are organized into plants or animals. In plants, most of the "sociology of cells" serves to make them more efficient in a sessile, autotrophic way of life. In animals, on the other hand, cells are so assembled and arranged that the resulting organism moves actively to obtain its food and to carry out other independent activities. Microbes and plants synthesize complex molecules and grow, but it is animals that *do* things. What they do and how they do it depends very largely on how they are constructed, what organs make up their bodies, and how their multitudes of cells are joined together into a stable, effective community of cooperating parts. It will be the central purpose of this book to outline as clear an understanding as modern science will allow of the ways in which cells are organized into animals.

THE ORGAN SYSTEMS OF ANIMALS

To analyze the workings of even one small part of an animal is surprisingly difficult, because so many events are taking place concurrently within microscopic dimensions. We can simplify the task by considering the important functions one at a time, an approach facilitated by the fact that cells and organs are more or less specialized in an efficient division of labor to perform each of the several functions that are essential for every sort of animal. As a starting point it is convenient to distinguish eight major functional systems: *framework, digestion, respiration, mobility, internal transport, regulation of chemical composition, reproduction,* and *regulation of function.*

Animal bodies are held together in a recognizable shape that provides a framework for all other operations and processes. The outermost layers always form a skin of varying thickness and strength, and in many animals there is also a more rigid supporting system, or *skeleton*, either inside the body or associated with the skin. The nature of these supporting systems varies widely according to the needs of the animal and its basic organization.

With a supporting system to hold it in one piece, an animal's next most pressing need is some sort of fuel for its bodily machinery—in other words, *food*. This it must obtain from the outside world by some sort of positive action, after which the food must be processed in many ways before being taken into the body proper. This processing, called *digestion*, is the mechanical and chemical breaking up of raw food into molecules directly usable for the production of energy.

The food molecules delivered by the digestive system take part in complex chemical reactions in the many cells of an animal's body, yielding energy as well as supplying materials for growth. Along with food molecules most animals require a supply of oxygen, and the end products of the whole process are carbon dioxide and water in addition to energy. The obtaining of oxygen and the disposal of excess carbon dioxide are the chief functions of respiratory systems, usually *gills* in aquatic animals and *lungs* in those that live in air.

Having obtained a supply of energy, animals characteristically use much of it to move about. Both the relative motion of various parts of the animal and the locomotion of the whole animal require *muscles*, the operations of which can only be understood in terms of their organization at the visible level as well as the organization of the contractile protein molecules within specialized muscle cells.

Most animals of any size require a specialized circulatory system to transport many substances between their various organ systems. Blood vessels, hearts, and the valves that direct the flow of blood within them are often the most critically important organs—the ones whose failure causes death most rapidly.

The maintenance of life requires much more than the straightforward operations listed above, for living machinery is too complex to run without regulation and control. The chemical regulation of an animal's body fluids is especially important since only the correct solutions of salts and other small molecules will sustain the living processes. Thus in the most highly organized animals the composition of the body must be regulated with great precision if they are to function effectively. This regulation is carried out by organs often called *excretory* systems, which include the kidneys.

Successful as animals are at life, their machinery sooner or later wears out to the point of death. New animals have usually been produced in the meantime, however, and the whole process of reproduction requires a major share of the energies of mature animals. Yet it is not sufficient merely to construct exact replicas of the parents. Over the long course of evolution a more complicated process has been selected because it is better suited to perpetuate animals over time spans far longer than their individual lifetimes. This process is sexual reproduction, and the reasons for its superiority are set forth in *Genetics* and in *Evolution* of this series. Organized reproductive systems are required to supply the specialized cells called *gametes* that, under favorable conditions, fuse to form the beginning of a new animal. Many animals also have elaborate organs to care for the developing young.

A bundle of organs is still not an animal. Even though certain of these organs, such as the kidneys, regulate the chemical composition of the body fluids, there remains the problem of coordinating all the various activities of muscles and other organs. Many of these are rapid, requiring split-second adjustments and regulations; others are spread over hours or days and allow a more leisurely, though equally critical, balancing. In response to these needs there is a variety of mechanisms for regulating the contractions of muscles and the rates at which other organs function. Some of this regulation is achieved by dispatching molecular messengers called *hormones* from one part of the body to another. A whole system of *endocrine glands* is used to produce several hormones; some have widespread results whereas others regulate the long-term actions of specific organs. The coordination of rapid movements is achieved by more specialized signals that travel over the surface of nerve cells, and a distinct *nervous system* is present in most animals to provide for the thousands of such signals that must shuttle back and forth to keep its many parts performing correctly and at the proper coordinated rates. The nervous system, more than any other system, makes animals what they really are—independent operators, living organisms that do things on their own.

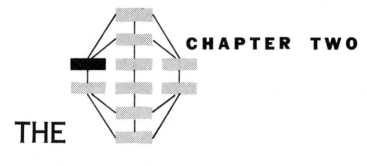

CHAPTER TWO

THE

BODY PLANS

OF ANIMALS
INTRODUCTION—For all their bewildering variety, animals are not infinitely diverse, and we need to understand only a few major types of body plans to obtain a useful frame of reference into which their varying structures and functional properties can readily be fitted. This is not accidental. Once the concept of evolution is accepted with understanding, it makes excellent sense to think of large numbers of related kinds of animals as descendants of one ancestral population. This common ancestry explains the basic similarity in body plan that characterizes the principal groups, or *phyla*, of animals. Descriptions of the major phyla and their probable relationships to one another may be found in *Evolution* and *Animal Adaptation* in this series.

DIVISION OF LABOR WITHIN SINGLE CELLS

Of all the body plans of animals the simplest is that of the animal-like microbes—namely, a single cell. These are often called *Protozoa*, and like all cells they have the following basic parts, starting from the outside and working inward: *cell membrane; cytoplasm,* containing *mitochondria, microsomes,* and other specialized components; and a *nucleus* surrounded by a nuclear membrane and containing a *nucleolus* and *chromosomes.* Even the nucleus is a multiple structure in many Protozoa, being separated into two or more parts having distinct functions. One nucleus may be specialized to hold the chromosomes containing the substance (*deoxyribonucleic acid,* abbreviated DNA) that carries the genetic "instructions" for the formation of almost identical new cells. Another nucleus may be specialized for the maintenance functions that all nuclei perform for the cytoplasm that contains them, providing a supply of a related substance (*ribonucleic acid,* or RNA) to aid in the synthesis of new protein. For a thorough description of the basic structure of a living cell, see *Cell Structure and Function* or *Microbial Life* in this series.

Protozoa often have skeletons, a fact that comes as a surprise to the student who naïvely believes that they are mere blobs of homogeneous jelly that somehow flow and move to catch food and maintain life. In some species of Protozoa grains of sand or other tiny particles adhere to a sticky external surface so that the cell comes to resemble a mobile croquette. Others have intricate internal skeletons formed by secreting an interconnected series of rods and plates. These may be surrounded by soft and mobile protoplasm, or the plates may form a protective outer shell provided with a few holes through which temporary tentacles of protoplasm are projected for feeding. Some of these skeletons are formed primarily of calcium carbonate ($CaCO_3$), others of silicon dioxide (SiO_2), and sometimes of still other materials, and they are often of truly beautiful shapes and patterns.

Digestive systems are also present in a group of Protozoa known as the ciliates, so named because over much of the cell surface they have hair-like structures called *cilia* that move back and forth rapidly to carry out swimming motions. Often an active ciliate pursues other microbes and engulfs them as food. Most ciliates have a more or less specialized part of the cell surface through which food is taken into the cytoplasm; usually this is a slight depression or groove. When a food particle is to be "swallowed," this part of the otherwise moderately stiff surface of the cell becomes softer, and the food moves through it along with a little of the surrounding water to become a *food vacuole* in the cytoplasm. Some ciliates have another specialized part of the cell membrane to serve as an *anus* through which undigested remains of the food are ejected.

Thus even within a single protozoan cell there is *intracellular* specialization—that is, the carrying out of a particular function by a specialized part of the cellular structure, which is appropriately called an *organelle*. Protozoa contain so many highly specialized organelles (some of which will be mentioned in later chapters) that it is often simpler to analyze such functions as digestion in multicellular animals where the division of labor is on a larger scale.

SIMPLE BUT EFFECTIVE COMMUNITIES OF CELLS

Unicellular plants often form small aggregates in which each cell functions almost exactly as it would alone. When multicellular animals are formed by the joining together of many cells, there are more stringent demands upon cooperation between cells; teamwork does not seem to pay on any large scale until the "team" reaches a considerable size. It seems to be more efficient either to remain unicellular (which has advantages for survival—for example, in the ease of dispersal and the minute size of the morsel a protozoan presents to predators) or to move toward multicellular organization and form an animal with fairly large organs each containing hundreds of cells. To be sure, all multicellular animals begin life as a single cell and are necessarily obliged to grow up through a series of immature stages involving increasing numbers of cells. But these developmental stages are often rushed through, often under specially protected or favorable circumstances, as though these were not efficient sizes or degrees of organization.

There is one fairly simple body plan that is often said to be the most successful of all, in that animals built according to its specifications bulk larger in total mass than any other group of multicellular animals. This plan in essence consists of a sack that is lined by a continuous layer of one sort of cell and whose outside covering is another layer of cells more suited for protection from the surrounding world. A closed sack would have no possibility of commerce with the world around it, and so in this efficient plan there is an opening into the inner cavity that serves as both mouth and anus; food is taken in through it and the same opening is used to eliminate undigested residues. This body plan is characteristic of the phylum *Coelenterata*, which means sacklike animals. To this phylum belong the jellyfish and corals, along with many basically similar animals such as the fresh-water hydra and the sea anemones. (See Fig. 2-1.)

The mouth is surrounded by movable tentacles that are used to bring food into it. Within the inner cavity formed by the sacklike shape of the body much of the food is digested. Digestive enzymes are liberated into this cavity, which for this reason may well be called the digestive cavity, although it serves for other purposes as well. Some living cells lining the digestive cavity take food into their cytoplasm much as Protozoa do, but the organization of great numbers of cells into a large sack permits much larger prey to be taken and digested. Furthermore, this arrangement permits many cells to concentrate on other operations—for example, the movement of the tentacles. Amino acids and sugars resulting from the digestion of food within the digestive cavity are distributed through the ramifications of this cavity out into the tentacles. The division of labor is therefore a mutually effective one: cells of the tentacles operate to capture large prey, and cells lining the digestive cavity specialize to some extent in the digestion of food.

The cells of the inner and outer layers are specialized in many other ways. Some are muscle cells that move the tentacles, bend the main part of the body, or in times of danger contract both tentacles and body into a compact cylinder with the digestive cavity reduced to negligible volume. There are elongated nerve cells that coordinate these contractions, and specialized sensory cells respond to such different outside influences as mechanical

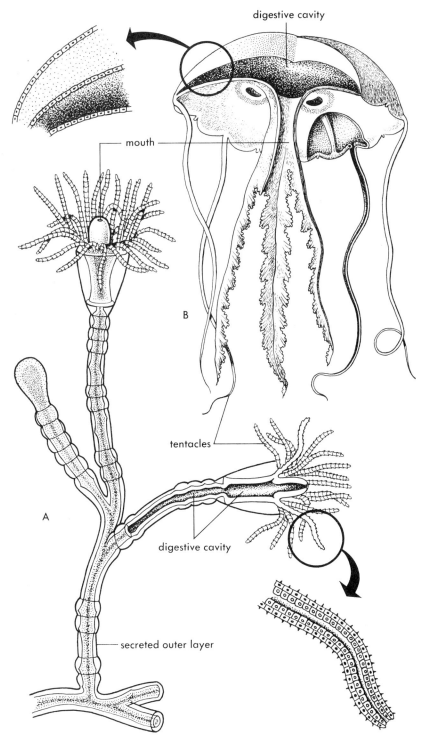

Fig. 2-1. Typical coelenterates: (A) a branching, colonial hydroid; (B) a medusa or jellyfish.

contact, gravity, and light. There are also cells that secrete protective layers over the outer surface of many coelenterates; an extreme example of such a layer is the hard, calcareous shell of the corals. The inner and outer layers may be one or more cells in thickness, and the two layers are not always in close proximity. In most coelenterates a jellylike substance is secreted by the cells of one or both layers to fill out the body wall between them to a greater thickness, and occasional cells may be dispersed in this jelly.

The coelenterate body plan has almost unlimited possibilities for expansion. The digestive cavity and the surrounding body wall, for example, may be long or short. Furthermore, one, two, or many mouths, with tentacles, may be formed from a common, branching digestive cavity. (See Fig. 2-1.) This arrangement is extended in many types of coelenterates into a branching colony with dozens or even hundreds of mouths, and in such a colony it is difficult to decide what constitutes the individual animal. Is it the single complex of mouth, tentacles, and adjacent digestive cavity, or is it the whole colony? If it is the former, such a coelenterate exists as a sort of multiple Siamese twin; if the latter, there is no definite limit to the size to which the branching, plantlike body may eventually grow. Although many of the coelenterates are attached to some substrate for most of their lives, others such as the jellyfishes are active swimmers. Here the sacklike body plan is modified to form an undulating, umbrellalike membrane surrounding the mouth, and it is by waves of contraction in this umbrella that the jellyfish swims. Despite their simple body plan and plantlike appearance, the coelenterates are animals composed of hundreds of specialized cells with division of labor among them. Many of their activities are directed toward movement and a heterotrophic way of life devoted to the capture of other living organisms as food.

THE FLATWORM BODY PLAN

For all their success in populating the seas and building coral reefs, coelenterates still remind us in many ways of plants. There is another large group of animals that wriggle and swim actively, and because of the flattened shape of the body are called flatworms (phylum Platyhelminthes). Many are parasites and live inside the bodies of other animals, but in striving for a concise view of major body plans we will concentrate on free-living members of this and other groups of animals. It is the digestive system that primarily distinguishes the flatworms from other wormlike animals; it has only a single opening, as in the coelenterates, whereas all other major groups of animals have a tubular digestive tract beginning with a mouth and ending with an anus through which undigested residues or feces are eliminated.

Coelenterates have no head or tail, and it is not even obvious what is

upper or lower surface. Instead they are symmetrical about a central axis—
that is, *radially symmetrical*. Flatworms, on the other hand, have a definite
head and usually move head first; they also have a preferred position, with
one surface upward and the other down or next to any surface with which
they may be in close contact. The single opening of the digestive tract is on
this lower, or as it is usually called, *ventral* surface (by derivation from the
Latin or Romance root meaning stomach). The opposite surface, usually
uppermost, is called *dorsal*, meaning back. The end of an animal where the
head is located is called the anterior end, the opposite end, the posterior.
This kind of a shape, where the right half is approximately a mirror image
of the left, is called *bilateral symmetry*. (See Fig. 2-2.)

This organization of the body into a bilateral symmetry is accompanied
by a concentration of the nervous system into the anterior end, and it is
primarily this concentration that distinguishes the front end as a head. Sense
organs, such as light-sensitive cells that form simple eyes, are most likely
to be found in the head, although in flatworms and many other animals
some light-sensitive cells are found elsewhere over the surface of the body.

Although there is only one opening from the digestive cavity to the
outside, only with difficulty can the body of a flatworm be conceived of as
a sack. The digestive cavity extends with branches and ramifications to
almost all parts of the ribbon-shaped body, and whole complex organs are
fitted between it and the outer skin. Aside from the nervous system, there
are also specialized organs for reproduction and for regulation of body fluids
that will be discussed in later chapters. Here the division of labor is not
merely between cells, as in the coelenterates; it is between organs.

THE ROUNDWORM BODY PLAN

The roundworms constitute a large group of wormlike animals
that differ from the flatworms in having a tubular digestive tract in which
food moves from mouth to anus, undergoing digestion on the way. Many
of the roundworms have a relatively large fluid-filled cavity between the body
wall and the digestive tract, and the latter, along with reproductive organs, is
suspended in this fluid with some freedom to move about within the body
as the worm twists and swims or wriggles. These worms often have specialized mouth parts with teeth for grasping food, and the digestive tract may
be somewhat specialized along its length for the processing of food. Basically,
though, the roundworms are just that, active cylindrical animals with a
definite head and a tubular digestive tract connecting mouth and anus. The
body cavity, distinct from the digestive tract and not connected with the
outside, serves many purposes including the circulation of its fluid contents
in a way that serves to move materials from one end of the worm to the

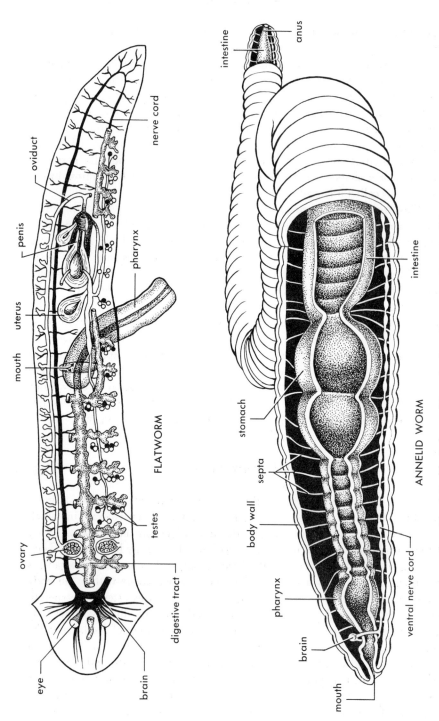

Fig. 2-2. Typical wormlike animals: a flatworm and an annelid worm.

other. Most of the roundworms are usually grouped into the phylum Nematoda, although there are many related groups and various experts classify them differently.

THE ANNELID BODY PLAN

Still a third group of worms differs from the roundworms in being segmented; that is, the body is formed as a series of short cylindrical units, connected together end to end and separated by partitions called *septa,* even though many of the organ systems run continuously through the septa from one segment to the next. The earthworm or night crawler is a familiar and widespread example of these animals, which are technically classified as the phylum Annelida. An annelid worm is like a roundworm or nematode in having a tubular digestive system running the length of the body from mouth to anus, but the several organ systems are much more highly elaborated. Circulatory and respiratory systems are present in a highly organized form in many annelids together with relatively massive and specialized nervous systems. More elaborate excretory systems regulate the fluid composition of the body, and the digestive tract is considerably specialized from mouth to anus into separate chambers where particular digestive processes occur more efficiently than would be possible if they were dispersed and intermingled along the length of an unspecialized tube. (See Fig. 2-2.) Each segment includes a relatively large fluid-filled body cavity in which the digestive tract and other organs are suspended, usually by membranes attached both to the organ itself and to the body wall.

The circulatory system of annelids such as the earthworm is almost as specialized in many ways as that of larger and more complex animals. Blood is pumped through tubular blood vessels by a series of muscular hearts, and the larger blood vessels branch to form thin-walled tubules in close proximity to active cells to which the blood brings needed materials. Some annelids have appendages that extend a short distance outward from several of the body segments and are used to help the animals move, either by swimming or crawling. In certain species these appendages are much longer and branch into thin tendrils filled with small blood vessels near the surface. These are *gills,* which serve to obtain oxygen from the surrounding water much more efficiently than it could be obtained through the smaller surface area of the body proper.

THE ARTHROPOD BODY PLAN

A segmented body plan containing specialized organs for all the major functions has proven its worth in the great number of very abundant animals that have lived and multiplied with this arrangement. A very effective

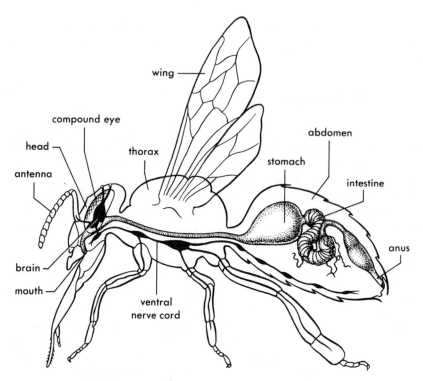

Fig. 2-3. Body plan of an insect (worker honeybee). (After Weber, H. *Grundriss der Insektenkunde*. Jena, Fischer, 1938.)

system of support has been obtained by addition to the annelid body plan of a stiff *exoskeleton* secreted around the outside of each body segment, and by an increase in length and complexity of the appendages, with a similar jointed exoskeleton around each segment of each leg. The phylum Arthropoda, built along these lines, is by far the largest group of animals that ever existed, in terms of numbers of species, and they are certainly our most serious competitors for the resources of the earth. This phylum includes the crustaceans such as lobsters, crabs, and shrimp, as well as the spiders and the insects. (See Fig. 2-3.) The major organ systems are all present and well developed, and respiratory systems in particular show some unique specializations that will be described in Chapter 5. The nervous system is a complex one, permitting a cleverness of behavior that is scarcely rivaled except by birds and mammals.

THE MOLLUSCAN BODY PLAN

The most familiar mollusks are the sedentary clams and oysters, which seem to be a distinct comedown after even the briefest consideration of the structure and behavior of such arthropods as the insects. There are, however, other members of the phylum Mollusca, such as snails and squids, that are surprisingly complex. The snails are notoriously slow travelers, but their internal organs are highly specialized; the class Cephalopoda that contains the squids (and the octopuses) represents an extreme specialization of the molluscan body plan for an active, free-swimming life. This plan is a compact one—a solid body containing a digestive tube with mouth and anus, reproductive and chemical-regulating or excretory systems, a nervous system, and in most cases organs for respiration. There are no appendages in any sense comparable to those of other groups of animals; instead there is a solid mass of muscle, called the foot, that serves for locomotion by a complicated series of partial contractions of its various sections. Its action resembles that of the human tongue in the variety of effective shapes it can assume. In the squids and octopuses the foot becomes subdivided into separate arms that move freely by well-controlled muscular contractions. These in turn require precise regulation, which is provided by a highly developed nervous system. The brain of an octopus is larger and more complicated in structure and function than that of any other group except the vertebrates. Basically, all the mollusks are constructed on a plan that entails compactness, the absence of paired appendages growing out from segments of the body, and finally by the secretion of a hard shell. The latter is prominent in clams, snails, and similar mollusks; in the squid and octopus the shell is largely internal and not nearly so conspicuous. (See Fig. 2-4.)

THE VERTEBRATE BODY PLAN

The remaining major pattern into which the organ systems of animals are arranged is our own, and that of a host of animals we intuitively recognize as more closely akin to us than insects, squids, or worms. Its most obvious feature is a jointed skeleton, deeply internal in contrast to the external jointed skeletons of the arthropods and the one- or two-piece secreted skeletons of the mollusks. This body plan we share with five clearly distinguishable groups of animals, all more or less familiar. These are (1) the other mammals, which also nurse their young, bear the young alive (with one or two interesting exceptions), have hair or fur as a body covering, and regulate the body temperature; (2) the feathered birds, most of which are highly specialized for flight, and which also regulate the body temperature but lay eggs and lack bony teeth; (3) the reptiles, which have scaly skins, do very little regulating of body temperature, have teeth that are not so specialized from one part of the mouth to another as in mammals, and lay birdlike eggs protected by a tough shell so that the embryos can develop on land within the protection of this shell; (4) the Amphibia, animals like frogs and

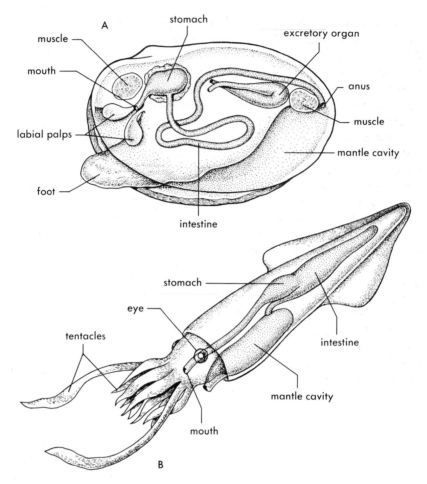

Fig. 2-4. Body plans of two important types of mollusk: (A) a clam; (B) a squid. The muscles shown in (A) serve to close the shell of the clam. The labial palps aid in bringing food particles to the mouth.

salamanders, which have a moist skin and must lay their eggs in water because they lack shells that can withstand drying. All of these four groups have the familiar two pairs of limbs and all have basically similar organ systems, including lungs for breathing air. Some of the Amphibia also have gills somewhat like those of fish. The fifth group is the fishes, which lack the limbs and have elaborate gills in place of lungs in order to obtain oxygen dissolved in water. Clearly the Amphibia are a transitional group intermediate between the purely aquatic fishes on the one hand and the terrestrial reptiles on the other.

Almost all of these vertebrate animals have the same type of internal skeleton. It is composed of bone, which is itself a unique material, formed by the secretions of thousands of specialized cells located close to small blood vessels of the circulatory system. Although it is hard and rigid, bone is more clearly a living organ than the secreted skeletons of other phyla. Furthermore, the bony skeletons of vertebrate animals are jointed, and the several bones are connected by appropriate types of living material to give the whole structure a flexibility that allows for a variety of movements and successful behavior.

The mutual relationships between the major organ systems in vertebrates are also quite different from those found in the arthropods or in other phyla. Not only is the nervous system the most complicated found in any group of animals, it is larger and more specialized and is located dorsal to the digestive tract rather than ventral as, for example, in the arthropods. There is no known reason why a dorsal location makes for a better nervous system, but this, like the flatness of the flatworms, is a convenient distinguishing feature. The four limbs of the terrestrial vertebrates are also supported by the same basic sort of a jointed, internal, body skeleton as the rest of the body, and although these limbs have become highly modified in many of the different kinds of vertebrate animals (or even lost altogether as in the snakes), they are all built according to a similar plan, as illustrated in Fig. 2-5.

An interesting attribute of the vertebrates is their ability to produce antibodies in their blood that combine with foreign proteins, and a few other types of large molecules, to protect the animal from injurious materials such as those often associated with bacterial infections. Only in our own phylum are these biochemical protective mechanisms well developed.

The vertebrate animals are considered members of the phylum *Chordata*, along with a few other groups of much simpler animals that share with some of the more primitive fishes and with early embryos of other vertebrates a type of axial skeleton called the *notochord*. This is a long cylindrical tube surrounded by connective tissue and filled with cells having a high proportion of water. It is located dorsal to the digestive tract but ventral to the vertebral column and spinal cord.

DEPARTURES FROM THE MAJOR BODY PLANS

This chapter has merely sketched in broadest outlines the body plans of the most successful and numerous phyla of animals. There are many others that have not been mentioned, and many members of these phyla have become so modified in the course of their evolutionary history that the characteristic body plan is obscured. This is particularly true of animals that have become specialized for a parasitic way of life or for life as attached or sessile forms.

To cite only one extreme example, one of the three subdivisions of the

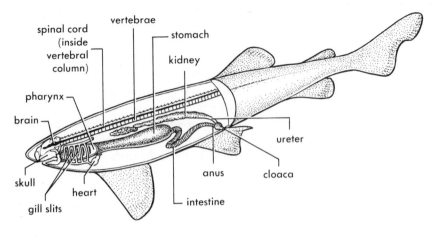

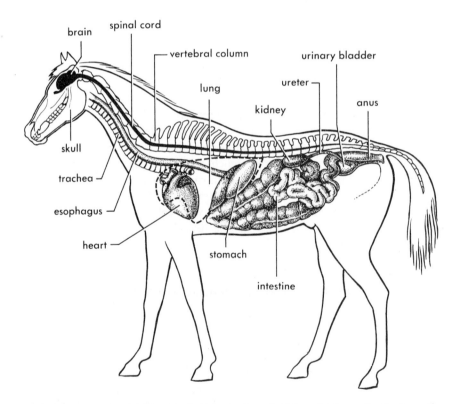

Fig. 2-5. Body plans of two vertebrate animals, a dogfish and a horse. In the horse the position of one lung is shown by a broken outline. In these and other vertebrates the central nervous system is enclosed within the skull and vertebral column.

flatworms (the class Cestoda) are the parasitic tapeworms. These animals live in the digestive tracts of vertebrate animals, attaching themselves by the head end to the wall of the host animal's intestine. The rest of the body is formed in segments, but these differ from the segments of the annelid worms in that no circulatory or digestive systems extend through the animal from one segment to the next. Indeed there is no digestive tract at all in the tapeworms. Living in an environment filled with partly digested food molecules, they can obtain all the food they need directly through the body wall, and they have lost altogether the digestive cavity that their presumed ancestors must have possessed at some remote and unfossilized stage in their evolutionary history. Although the degenerate specialization of the tapeworm is an extreme case, in studying the animals of the real world one must be prepared to find these basic body plans modified and altered to suit thousands of special needs.

SUGGESTED READING LIST

BERRELL, N. J. "The indestructible hydra," *Scientific American*, Dec. 1957, p. 118.

BORRADAILLE, L. A., POTTS, F. A. and EASTMAN, F. A., 1959. *The invertebrates*, 3d ed. Cambridge, Eng.: Cambridge University Press.

BROWN, M. E., ed., 1957. *The physiology of fishes*, vols. I and II. New York: Academic Press.

BUCHSBAUM, R., 1948. *Animals without backbones*. Chicago: University of Chicago Press.

HOCKING, B. "Insect flight," *Scientific American*, Dec. 1958, p. 92.

MORTON, J. E., 1958. *Molluscs*. London: Hutchinson.

PARKER, T. J., and HASWELL, W. A., 1951. *A textbook of zoology*, 6th ed., vols. I and II. London: Macmillan.

RAMSAY, J. A., 1952. *A physiological approach to the lower animals*. Cambridge, Eng.: Campridge University Press.

ROMER, A. S., 1959. *The vertebrate story*. Chicago: University of Chicago Press.

STEINBACH, H. B. "The squid," *Scientific American*, Apr. 1951, p. 64.

WATERMAN, T. H., ed., 1960-61. *The physiology of crustacea*. New York: Academic Press.

WILLIAMS, C. M. "The metamorphosis of insects," *Scientific American*, Apr. 1950, p. 24.

YOUNG, J. Z., 1950. *The life of vertebrates*. New York: Oxford University Press.

———, 1957. *The life of mammals*. New York: Oxford University Press.

CHAPTER THREE

STRUCTURAL

SYSTEMS INTRODUCTION—Protoplasm is more than two-thirds

water, but living organisms are far from being liquid. Not only do they maintain a fairly definite shape, but they keep their body fluids in a chemical state that differs markedly from the surrounding media in which they live. The structural systems considered in this chapter are those parts that enable animals to hold a particular shape, both when at rest and when engaged in their various activities. It is convenient to begin with aquatic animals, not only because the earliest living organisms almost certainly lived in sea water, but because their problems of support are the simplest.

STRUCTURAL INTEGRITY IN AQUATIC ANIMALS

Any animal living in the water has an immediate advantage over one that lives in air, because protoplasm has almost the same density as water and hence an aquatic animal is in little danger of collapsing under the influence of gravity. For example, a jellyfish, having much the consistency of a very thin gelatin dessert, when stranded on a beach will flow and droop into a flat blob bearing little resemblance to the beautiful shape that floats in the water. Even a large whale, though it is a mammal with a sturdy internal skeleton, is hard put to hold its shape if stranded by the falling tide, because its supporting system is not well suited for holding in place several tons of soft flesh without the aid of surrounding water of nearly the same density.

Even though aquatic animals have relatively little need for support against gravity, they must all protect themselves from too rapid and free an exchange of their constituent molecules with the water around them. Since the same solvent is present inside and out, a sodium ion or a glucose molecule near the animal's surface can diffuse out into the environment as well as inward. Hence even the simplest of animals possess some sort of skin that is relatively impermeable to water and to the dissolved molecules that make up protoplasm. But an animal cannot afford to wall itself off behind a totally impervious membrane, for it must obtain some molecules such as food and oxygen from the outside, and other substances must be eliminated lest they accumulate in excessive concentrations within the cytoplasm. The essence of a living surface is thus a balance between too much permeability and too little, between allowing the escape of too much useful material and impeding too greatly the intake of needed molecules.

SKIN

In the more specialized multicellular animals skin is composed of one or more layers of specialized cells, usually flattened and having relatively small nuclei. Often these cells secrete stronger materials than typical cell membranes. These materials may be mucus (a special type of polysaccharide called mucopolysaccharides), horny, or leathery insoluble and fibrous proteins, gelatinous material that also gains its consistency from a more dispersed series of elongated protein molecules such as those of collagen, and finally a variety of sturdy materials that may be secreted in or on the outer surface of the skin as particles or plates somewhat separated from the cells that formed them. The roundworms (phylum Nematoda) have an outer layer of fused cells that form a nearly continuous sheet; nuclei are interspersed here and there, but the protoplasm is not subdivided by cell membranes. Such an arrangement is called a *syncytium*. This syncytial cuticle, as it is called, has a relatively tough outer "cell" wall and tends, as do the skins of many aquatic animals, to secrete a thin layer of mucus over the outer surface of the animal.

SKELETONS

Being encased in a skin of limited permeability is not enough for the successful adaptation of many animals to a variety of ways of life. Internal and external skeletons are found even in some of the Protozoa, and among the coelenterates the corals are famous for their externally secreted skeletons. None of the worms—flat, round, or segmented—have developed important skeletons, although some of the annelid worms secrete material around their bodies in the form of protective tubes. Highly developed skeletons are thus restricted to the three most specialized phyla, the Mollusca, the Arthropoda, and the Vertebrata, and these three have employed radically different plans for their skeletons, just as their basic body plans differ in many other ways. The differences between the three may conveniently be analyzed in terms of the material from which the skeleton is formed, the anatomical position of the skeleton relative to the other organs of the body, and the arrangements for articulation of the separate elements of the skeleton to one another.

The skeletons of mollusks are mainly composed of calcium carbonate ($CaCO_3$), an ubiquitous substance that takes on quite different properties in the shell of a clam or snail from those of $CaCO_3$ in marble or limestone rock. The molluscan shell is secreted by cells on the outer surface of the body, progressively in layers as the animal itself grows. Protein fibers are also laid down between layers of $CaCO_3$, and other organic substances are interspersed in smaller concentrations to give the whole structure a considerably greater strength per unit weight than would be found in pure $CaCO_3$. The shells usually have an outer layer of more horny material that contains a greater proportion of protein. Pigments may be present to give the shells of snails a variety of patterns and colors.

Although to a chemist who analyzes it by routine methods a clamshell may seem to be little more than calcium carbonate (with a few traces of "impurities" such as proteins), a study of its microscopic structure reveals an elaborate organization reflecting its secretion by living cells. This organization gives the shell more efficient properties, making it better adapted for its original purpose of supporting and protecting the body that formed it. The shells of mollusks are enlarged by the addition of new secreted material near their outer edges. The cells lying just under the outer lip of a clamshell are constantly adding new secreted material, rapidly when food is plentiful and conditions favorable, more slowly if times are hard. Other cells lying just under the older part of the shell, nearer to the hinge, add more material to increase its thickness, and the patterns in which $CaCO_3$ and protein fibers are laid down differ according to the age and thickness.

Arthropods form their external skeletons as plates on the outer surface of the body and appendages. These plates are composed of a hard material secreted by a layer of living cells just beneath the exoskeleton. The exoskeleton of an insect is a good example, although other arthropods differ only in relatively minor ways. As illustrated in Fig. 3-1, the living cells that form the hard covering are a single layer, most of them relatively unspecialized. Each one secretes a variety of materials as the cuticle is formed. First to be secreted, and hence outermost, on the finished surface, is a waxy layer with protein interspersed; underneath this, and formed somewhat later, is a harder layer containing not only the ubiquitous fibrous proteins but a material called *chitin* that is especially characteristic of insect exoskeletons, although it is also found in the hard parts of several other groups of animals, including coelenterates, annelid worms, and mollusks. Only in the arthropods, however, is it widely used to stiffen a jointed exoskeleton. Chitin is chemically related to sugars and polysaccharides, being composed of many units having the same molecular structure as glucose but with an $NHCOCH_3$ group replacing one of the OH groups of the glucose molecule. Chitin is insoluble

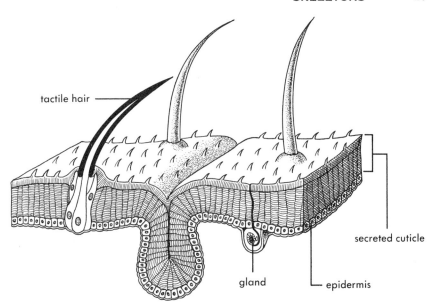

tactile hair

secreted cuticle

gland   epidermis

Fig. 3-1. The skin and cuticle of an insect (after H. Weber, *Grundriss der Insekten-kunde.* Jena, Fischer, 1938). The cuticle contains the chitin that stiffens the exoskeleton.

in every ordinary solvent, as is cellulose, the major material of plant cell walls—the material that is separated from suitable plant fibers to make cotton, paper, and a variety of useful materials. Cellulose is made up as a polymer of glucose units in the same way that chitin is a polymer of similar groups containing the nitrogen atom.

In the exoskeletons of insects and other arthropods the chitin is closely bound to protein molecules, and this combination gives the uniquely strong, flexible, and resilient properties to the actual skeleton in the living animal. The chitinous plates are not uniform from point to point but are contoured to form an efficient armor—thinner where bending occurs, thicker and reinforced by spines and ridges where a stiffener is required. Furthermore, at intervals there are small holes through which protrude horny stiff hairs; these are not rigidly fused to the exoskeleton itself but are free to move slightly in a socket formed by one or more of the specialized cells surrounding the cell that forms the hair. Often there are nerve cells closely associated with the base of a hair; these are sensitive to minute movements of the hair, sometimes even to the submicroscopic deflections caused by sound waves or vibrations of the ground or vegetation signaling the approach of some other animal. At the joints between the plates of an insect's exoskeleton the hardened chitinous layers are absent, but the thinner, more flexible, waxy and leatherlike outer layers are continuous through the region of the joint. Thus an insect's skin is a continuous one over all parts of the body, though it is interrupted, as shown in Fig. 3-1, by openings of glands and by various openings concerned with the respiratory, digestive, and reproductive systems. What makes the exoskeleton jointed is the sectional stiffening of the skin by hard plates formed by a complex interweaving of chitin and protein molecules.

The Molting of Arthropods

The arthropod exoskeleton suffers from one serious limitation. Once laid down, the chitinous plates seem to be relatively permanent, and the insect (or a crustacean such as a crab or lobster) can only grow by a process of molting. In the course of molting, the exoskeleton first becomes somewhat softened by a breakdown of the chitinous plates, presumably caused by some chemical activity of the layer of living cells just beneath. These cells then grow in size and sometimes undergo cell division as well. The remains of the old exoskeleton are shed, either in one piece or by splitting into several fragments, and finally new and larger plates are deposited in their place. During the interval between the shedding of the old and the hardening of the new plates the animal continues to be encased in a soft flexible skin, but being soft bodied it is vulnerable both to predators and to injury from environmental influences such as drying. The soft-shelled crab is a normally well-armored arthropod, that is temporarily in this embarrassingly defense-less stage. Moderately large *terrestrial* arthropods such as certain land crabs are especially helpless while molting, and if such an animal were as large as a dog, its soft body would probably collapse like a stranded jellyfish.

No one has yet discovered why arthropods must go through this danger-ous phase of complete replacement of their all-important exoskeletons in several successive molts as they grow larger. Other animals, as will be ex-plained in the next section, have arrangements for efficient piecemeal growth, replacement, and even reorganization involving changes in shape of their skeletons. Many insects do achieve a considerable degree of breakdown dur-ing molting of the chitin-protein complex in their exoskeletons. Why these cells do not rebuild the same plates in a slightly larger size, rather than dis-carding them, is one of the unsolved problems of biology. This limitation of the way in which an arthropod's exoskeleton is organized for growth seems to be one of the major factors preventing the attainment of large body size, at least in terrestrial forms. In view of the frightful efficiency of insects and the serious nature of their competition, we may be thankful for this handi-cap under which they operate.

Vertebrate Endoskeletons

Vertebrate animals are the only ones that possess highly developed and efficient *internal* skeletons that are jointed and provide both stiffening and support for the body and at the same time permit movement of the parts thus strengthened. The aquatic vertebrates, of which the most abundant and the first to appear in geological history were the fishes, benefit from their internal skeletons principally in being able to attach rather sturdy muscles to a firm yet jointed framework against which these muscles in turn can pull. The swimming of a small fish is far more rapid and efficient than that of an aquatic worm of the same size; although other organ systems of the fish are also superior to those of the worm, the internal skeleton is a major factor in the aquatic efficiency of the former over the latter. Terrestrial animals of any size have much more pressing needs for skeletal support, however, because their bodies are much more dense than the surrounding air; hence it is on land that the internal skeleton of the vertebrates pays the largest dividends.

The earliest fishlike vertebrates known from fossils had bony armor as well as an internal skeleton, but nothing is known about their ancestors, which probably had less easily fossilized skeletons. In addition to bone, vertebrate skeletons often employ to varying degrees a material called *cartilage,* which is a tough, but slightly flexible and often quite elastic substance whose mechanical properties can be judged by the simple experiment of bending one's own ears (they are stiffened by cartilage). These two materials in varying proportions, and with different degrees of interspersal of living cells and softer material, form the skeletons of all vertebrate animals.

If a bone is analyzed chemically, one finds that after as much as possible of the soft tissue in and around it has been removed, its chief components are a complex of the salts $Ca_3(PO_4)_2$ and $CaCO_3$. The proportions are close to those of a common mineral, apatite, but the actual nature of bone is quite different from that of any homogeneous salt or mineral. For one thing, even the densest bone is not one continuous piece. The inorganic material is laid down by and around living cells, and these cells are present even in mature bone, together with blood vessels and other living cells. Bone is thus riddled by a continuous interconnected series of small canals with minute branches (see Fig. 3-2), in which these cells live and interchange materials with the blood as well as with the solid matrix in which they have entombed themselves. The secreted material is not composed solely of hard inorganic salts but contains much fibrous protein similar to that secreted by connective tissue, described in the next section. It is important to realize, aside from its complex heterogeneity, that bone is a living organ or tissue and that material can be subtracted as well as added to the inert mass of secreted salts and proteins. As bones grow, the relative proportions of the various major components—live cells, blood vessels, secreted protein, and inorganic salts—all can undergo changes with time. Thus a bone that was quite soft and spongy in youth may become hard and nearly solid in maturity, and in old age the hard material is often gradually removed, leaving brittle and greatly weakened the bone that was once remarkably sturdy.

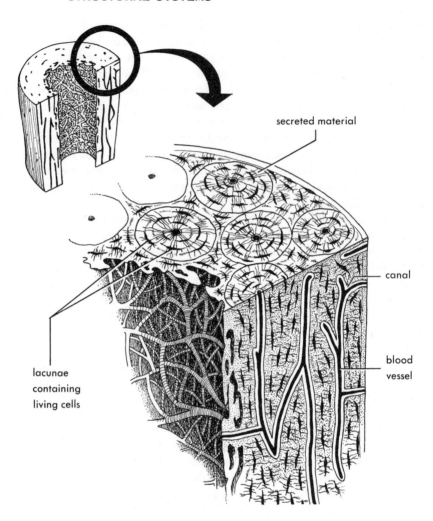

secreted material

canal

blood
vessel

lacunae
containing
living cells

Fig. 3-2. The microscopic structure of bone. Living cells located in the lacunae secrete the hard material of the bone, and their needs are supplied by blood vessels.

Cartilage is also the product of secretory activities by living cells that have surrounded themselves with it. It varies greatly in properties, ranging from a very stiff type to an elastic type. In the former, the cells are widely scattered singly or in small groups, and the secreted matrix is largely composed of a complex of protein and a modified carbohydrate called chondroitin. This substance, like chitin, contains glucose units in which an OH group is replaced by $NHCOCH_3$, and other glucose units that have sulfate groups attached. At the other extreme of a series of different kinds of cartilage, the elastic type has a greatly increased proportion of elastic protein fibers. Our external ears are supported by elastic cartilage, whereas the softer extensions of many bones (such as the human nose) contain the less flexible type. In young animals of all groups of vertebrates much or all of the skeleton is composed of cartilage, and in one major group of fishes—the sharks and their relatives—it forms the whole skeleton of even the adult fish.

THE ORGANIZED SKELETON

The materials comprising vertebrate skeletons are formed into characteristic units, usually called "bones" for convenience, although, as noted above, in certain animals the skeletons may be composed of cartilage. Most prominent is the skull—essentially a box containing the brain—with jaws, the upper one part of the skull proper and the lower one hinged or articulated to allow opening and shutting as well as chewing movements. Next most important is the *vertebral column,* or backbone, formed by a number of separate vertebrae, each containing a central hole through which runs the *spinal cord,* the main dorsal part of the nervous system. The skull

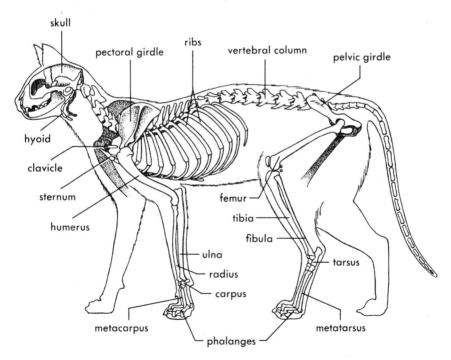

Fig. 3-3. The skeleton of a representative mammal, the housecat, with its principal bones labeled.

and vertebral column constitute the *axial skeleton,* and they surround and protect the central nervous system—that is, the brain and spinal cord. Lateral from the central portion of the vertebral column there are paired ribs that are usually joined to the vertebrae and form curved spars that give support to the chest, or *thoracic* region of the trunk. In most vertebrates there are two pairs of appendages, which have jointed bones to provide their internal skeleton, and these are connected to the vertebral column via somewhat larger bones of specialized shape, the *pelvic* and *pectoral girdles.* Fig. 3-3 shows the principal parts of the skeleton of the cat, together with the technical names. These anatomical terms are very few in number compared with the multitude that are used by biologists to designate all the many bones and parts thereof. Just as the names of animal groups are minimized in this introductory book in order not to obscure the principles of organization underlying the superbly efficient functional systems of animal bodies, so the names of a multitude of parts have been severely reduced. Once the main ideas of animal organization are understood it is not difficult to turn at need to reference books to find the names by which individual parts are known in more advanced and technical sources of biological information. The relatively few terms that *are* included here, however, are so widely used that any student who does not know them will be severely handicapped in studying biology.

CONNECTIVE TISSUE

A skeleton is more than a set of individual bones and cartilages; indeed, all of the individual parts and organs of any animal would fall apart were it not for the cells and inert secreted materials that comprise connective tissue. The term "tissue" is used here and elsewhere to denote a more or less continuous set of cells and their adjacent secretion products that act together for some definite purpose. In almost all multicellular animals a variety of cells take part in this important function of connecting one part of the body to another. Usually these connective tissue cells are rather elongated and their protoplasm may form radiating branches that can change in shape slowly over hours or days. (See Fig. 3-4.) Close around them, these cells secrete fibrous, gelatinous, and sticky, mucuslike materials to form sheets, strings, or masses of living tissue that serves the joining and linking function of connective tissue. One of the most important of these materials is the class of proteins known as *collagen,* which exists in the form of long fibers and has a well-defined ultrastructure enabling it to be recognized in electron microscope pictures of many types of living material.

The thicker and tougher parts of skin are a type of connective tissue in which insoluble fibrous proteins predominate. Equally important are the

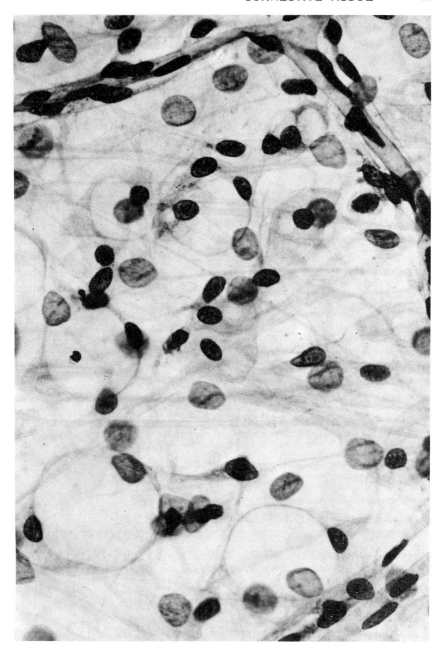

Fig. 3-4. Photomicrograph of typical connective tissue. Note the several types of connective tissue cells and the various fibers they have secreted. A capillary containing numerous red blood cells is also included. (Courtesy of D. Fawcett, Harvard Medical School.)

many membranes that line various cavities in the bodies of animals, and the cordlike or sheetlike *ligaments* and *tendons* that connect together bones and muscles. Wherever muscles and skeletal elements are connected together it can be assumed that a specialized kind of connective tissue is responsible. Connective tissue also fills in chinks and spaces in various parts of animal bodies, and one special type includes cells with a large amount of fat contained in globules in the cytoplasm. These cells serve as places for the storage of fat that is drawn upon in times of need when food is not available from the outside. Fatty connective tissue is also important as a soft padding between many organs.

Connective tissue may at first thought seem to be merely stuffing and packaging for the real organs, but actually it must be considered a far more refined phenomenon. Millions of relatively simple cells scattered all over the body are capable of secreting a wide variety of materials of differing mechanical properties; yet each group of connective tissue cells does in fact secrete only the correct materials and these in appropriate amounts. Those just under the skin produce insoluble fibrous proteins such as collagen and keratin to form the hide, whereas cells not very different in appearance form almost nothing but collagen if they are located near joints or at the junction of a muscle and a bone. Hundreds of different mechanical needs are filled by these versatile cells and the substances they secrete. If they elaborate the wrong materials or the incorrect proportions, the body is severely handicapped; yet, on the whole, such errors do not happen. Hence we must conclude that despite its lack of any visible pattern of structure such as that found in a bone, connective tissue is far from being a random stuffing. Even these cells are organized to function efficiently at a multitude of diversified and essential tasks.

SUGGESTED READING LIST

McLean, F. C. "Bone," *Scientific American*, Feb. 1955, p. 84.

Maximow, A. A. and Bloom, W. A., 1957. *A textbook of histology*, 7th ed. Philadelphia: Saunders. Chapters 4-7.

Montagna, W., 1956. *The structure and function of skin*. New York: Academic Press.

Murray, P. D. F., 1936. *Bones*. Cambridge, Eng.: Cambridge University Press.

Wigglesworth, V. B., 1953. *Principles of insect physiology*, 5th ed. London: Methuen. Chapter 2.

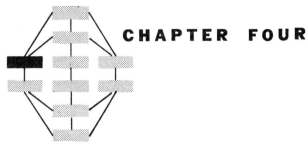

DIGESTIVE

SYSTEMS INTRODUCTION—Securing and processing food is obviously one of the most important functions to be performed by any animal, and the ease or difficulty of the task varies enormously according to the animal's way of life. At one extreme of nutritional security are intestinal parasites for which the host animal does all the work of catching the food and most of the digesting as well. In consequence, the most highly organized of these intestinal parasites, the tapeworms, have no digestive system; food molecules such as sugars simply diffuse from the intestinal contents of the host into the body of the tapeworm. Most animals, however, must work for their living, and much of their immediate business is securing food and chemically reducing it to small molecules that can move into their bodies.

Protozoa take food particles across the cell membrane by engulfing them or by temporarily opening up a hole through this normally continuous surface membrane. Similar engulfing of particles also occurs in many cells of multicellular animals. In coelenterates and many other invertebrate animals, cells detach themselves from the wall of the digestive cavity, move about in its contents, engulf food particles, then return to the animal's tissue, move about within it, and presumably give off some products of digestion to other cells —although the details of this process have never been determined. Such wandering cells are much like a common protozoan, the *amoeba*, which has a rather fluid protoplasm and changes its shape from moment to moment by extending temporary projections or contracting into a nearly spherical form. Hence these cells are called *amoebocytes*. In our own bodies and those of all other animals, cells of this general type circulate in the blood and tissue fluids, moving about through the spaces between other cells and often engulfing such foreign particles as bacteria. They are the *phagocytes* (including most types of white blood cells), which form part of our resistance to infection.

When food is digested inside a single cell it lies in a vacuole or fluid-filled cavity in the cytoplasm. As far as we know, the essential steps in the process of digestion are the same whether they occur in a food vacuole in an amoebocyte or in the large and visibly specialized digestive tract of a mammal. These steps have been much more thoroughly studied in the multi-cellular animals, and we can best consider them in animals in which division of labor has segregated the major processes into separate locations.

All animals more specialized than the flatworms have a tubular digestive tract leading from an anterior mouth to a posterior opening, the *anus*, through which food residues or *feces* are eliminated. There is an obvious efficiency to a digestive system that is subdivided into sequentially specialized stages, each carried out by an organ, such as the mouth, stomach, or intestine, that is suited for a particular process. Food is coveted not so much for itself as because it supports the life of the animal that eats it; feces are therefore the ultimate in undesirability, because almost everything of value to the animal has been removed.

DIVISION OF LABOR ALONG THE DIGESTIVE TRACT

Digestion begins with mechanical fragmentation of the food by chewing. A wide variety of toothlike structures are used by different kinds of animals both to seize food initially and to reduce it to small particles. In birds, however, most of the reduction is accomplished in a modified part of the stomach—the crop or gizzard; birds have no bony teeth, and the horny bill can cut food into only slightly smaller pieces. The crop is a muscular chamber that squeezes and kneads the food, and in most birds small stones or grit are swallowed and held in this chamber to aid in the process. Eventually the hard particles are worn smooth and perhaps reduced in size, until finally they pass along through the digestive tube and must be replaced; this is why seed-eating birds such as chickens will starve to death on a full stomach unless they have a supply of grit. Other animals including earthworms and some kinds of insects employ some internal mechanical fragmentation in their stomachs, and in almost all animals some muscular churning supplements chemical digestion. A chemical attack on food particles is possible only at their surfaces, and the rate of chemical digestion depends in large part on the breaking up of large pieces into a number of smaller ones with a greater total surface area.

Even flatworms and coelenterates have a more or less specialized mouth, and many of the free-living, as opposed to the parasitic, flatworms have a rather complicated proboscis at the mouth that they push out to engulf food and at other times retract into the digestive cavity. Many of the roundworms and annelid worms have hard, sharp, or barbed teeth at the entrance to their mouths, and the arthropods have highly elaborate jaws and teeth for seizing prey and breaking up animal or vegetable food. Many of the mollusks have a characteristic type of rasping structure, called the *radula,* that is moved back and forth by muscles and that scrapes and files away at foods or sources of food even though they may be extremely hard and resistant. Certain snails, for example, drill holes through the hard shells of other mollusks such as oysters in order to eat the soft parts of the prey, which is often much larger than the attacking snail. A few mollusks have carried this process so far that the radula is used to dig out burrows into wood or even rock.

In mammals the saliva contains a digestive enzyme that begins the chemical digestion of starch to maltose in the mouth, but this is rather exceptional, aside from instances to be discussed below where food is digested before being taken into the mouth. In all animals with a "through-track" digestive tube, food is moved from the mouth cavity into a stomach that is usually enlarged to form a chamber where food can be stored temporarily and also undergo chemical digestion. At the posterior end of the stomach there is almost always a muscular valve called a sphincter; that is, a narrow part of the digestive tube that can be closed by the action of muscles arranged in a ring around the tube.

The next section of the digestive tract is the intestine, and in all animals it is the portion from which almost all of the digested food molecules are absorbed into the body. The material that enters the intestine from the stomach is largely liquid; any remaining solid particles are quite small and are often indigestible residues that will be passed out in the feces. Digestive glands are very prominent in or near the walls of the intestine, and their products are of great importance in completing the processes of chemical digestion. In animals with well-developed circulatory systems there is a rich blood supply to the walls of the intestine in order that the food molecules absorbed from the cavity or lumen of the intestine can be carried off.

The more posterior parts of the digestive tract are often specialized for the absorption of water, so that the contents are made drier and harder. Often another feature of this part of the digestive tract is the large populations of bacteria and other microorganisms. Many animals have branches from the large intestine called *caeca* (sing. *caecum*) and food residues may remain there for some time undergoing chemical changes caused by the microorganisms. (See Fig. 4-1.) Finally, there is often a rectum or more muscular chamber where the feces accumulate and are periodically extruded through the anus. A muscular sphincter keeps the anus closed except during defecation.

Animals that feed largely on other animals, and hence obtain much of their fuel from molecules much like those in their own bodies, usually have shorter and simpler digestive tracts with only small caeca if any. Herbivorous animals have a harder task of chemical digestion and must hold food under digestion for longer periods and in more elaborately subdivided stomachs or large caeca where food material is held while microbes digest cellulose to sugars that are utilized both by them and by the host animal.

A

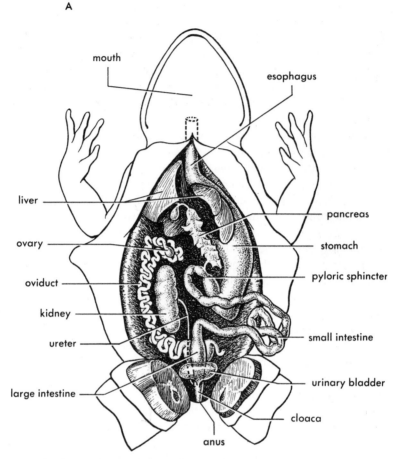

Fig. 4-1. Digestive tract of (A) a frog, and (B) a rabbit. The intestinal tract of the rabbit is more complicated, because it is a mammal and because it is herbivorous in contrast to the carnivorous frog. In the frog the bile duct and the pancreatic duct enter the small intestine together.

Digestive tracts in more highly specialized animals such as mammals often have folds and inward projections that serve to increase the surface area through which food may be transferred into the blood. The most important of these surface-increasing structures are the *villi* (sing. *villus*), which are found in enormous numbers on the inner surface of the mammalian small intestine. Each villus is a finger-shaped projection inward from the surface of the intestinal tube; in the interior of the villus are blood vessels into which the products of digestion are transferred by a process discussed below, generally designated as absorption. (See Fig. 4-2.) Owing to the presence of villi, the total surface area for absorption is many times what

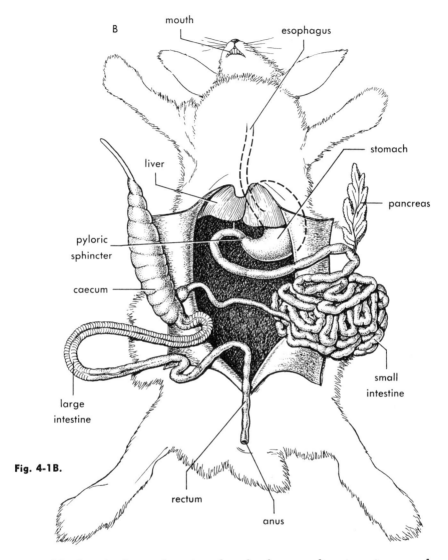

Fig. 4-1B.

it would otherwise be, and a given length of mammalian intestine can absorb much more food than it could were it a simple tube. The surfaces of the cells forming the innermost surface of the intestine are folded into *microvilli*, which are clearly visible only with the aid of the electron microscope. These minute projections also serve to increase the surface area available for the processes that enable these cells to move digested food from the contents of the intestine to the blood vessels that will carry it to other parts of the body.

Digestive glands are essential in all parts of all digestive systems. They

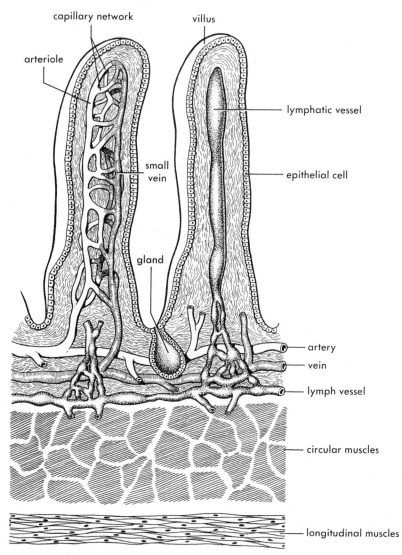

Fig. 4-2. Microscopic structure of two adjacent villi from the intestine of a mammal. For simplicity the capillaries and lymphatic vessels are shown as simple tubes, though their walls are actually composed of flattened cells.

vary from single cells that line the digestive cavity and that discharge mucus or digestive enzymes directly into the cavity, to cells formed into large separate organs; these organs discharge their secretions into ducts that are in turn connected to other ducts to form tubules draining eventually into the cavity or the digestive tract. The largest digestive glands of vertebrate animals are the pancreas and the liver, both of which drain into the small intestine.

Food is needed by animals for two reasons: to provide energy and to furnish specific molecules needed in small amounts to maintain growth or life itself. Among these molecules are the vitamins, some of which are discussed in *Cell Structure and Function,* in this series, in terms of their importance to the biochemical processes that occur within all cells. Although a wide variety of animal and plant material can be used to fuel the bodily machinery of animals, the great bulk of foods actually utilized falls into three classes—*carbohydrates, fats,* and *proteins.*

CARBOHYDRATES

The molecule most widely used as a source of energy by living organisms is *glucose,* and its oxidation can be summarized by the chemical equation

$$C_6H_{12}O_6 + 6O_2 \to \to \to \to 6CO_2 + 6\,H_2O + \text{energy}$$

The series of small arrows indicates that many steps intervene between the initial stage, when only sugar and oxygen are present, and the final products shown at the right.

Most of the carbohydrates found in the bodies of animals are polysaccharides or polymers of simple sugars—usually glucose joined to another glucose, this in turn to a third, and so on until a huge molecule containing hundreds of glucose units is built up. Water is removed as each bond between successive glucose units is formed, and the formation of a typical carbohydrate can thus be represented in its barest essentials by the reaction

$$n(C_6H_{12}O_6) \to \to \to \to (C_6H_{10}O_5)_n + nH_2O$$

Among the most common carbohydrates are (1) the glycogens, which are formed in the cells of animals; (2) the starches, which are formed in plant cells, particularly in those devoted to storage of food for the plant; and (3) cellulose, which is a much more stable and indigestible polymer formed by a different type of bond between successive glucose molecules (also involving the loss of water). Thus the formula $(C_6H_{12}O_6)_n$ serves only to identify carbohydrates as a class and not to distinguish between them; it describes equally well the main constituent of flour (starch) or of paper (cellulose). Chitin, the main stiffening constituent of insect exoskeletons discussed in Chapter 3, is a modified carbohydrate, but its oxidation is also an energy-yielding reaction, and hence certain animals are able to use chitin as a food.

When most animals eat food containing polysaccharides these large molecules are not taken directly into the cytoplasm from food vacuoles or through the cells of a specialized digestive tract. Instead they are broken down either to the simple sugars such as glucose, or to smaller polymers containing two or three glucose units, or, in the case of some polysaccharides, to slightly different sugar units about the size of glucose. It is simple sugars, containing 5 or 6 carbon atoms, that are the units of carbohydrate actually taken into the bodies of animals from the digested food.

Large carbohydrate polymers can be broken down to glucose units in a test tube, but only by such means as boiling with strong acids; in the digestive systems of animals the process occurs at low temperatures and without the need for violent reagents. *Digestive enzymes* are the agents responsible for this gentler but more effective process—specifically, carbohydrate-digesting enzymes sometimes called *carbohydrases*. These are specialized protein molecules having the important property of catalyzing the breaking up of the large molecule of carbohydrate into smaller polymers and finally to glucose molecules, or units of similar size. Human saliva contains a type of carbohydrase that breaks down starch only part way and only by attacking one type of bond that joins together chains of sugar molecules; hence the result of its activity is a group of smaller polymers. Other carbohydrases can perform a complete breakdown with only glucose as the end products; examples are those secreted by the pancreas of most vertebrate animals. None of these carbohydrases act on cellulose; only microorganisms produce *cellulase* to digest this widespread but very stable carbohydrate.

FATS

Fats are compounds of fatty acids and glycerol ($CH_2OHCHOHCH_2OH$), which is an alcohol with three OH groups. Each fatty acid consists of a long chain of carbon atoms attached to as many hydrogen atoms as possible, with an organic acid or COOH group at the end of the chain—for example, $CH_3(CH_2)_{15}COOH$. In the formation of a fat, three fatty acids combine with the three OH groups of glycerol in a kind of acid-base reaction with the elimination of water; the resulting fat is an ester or organic acid "salt." The carbon chain of the fatty acids is about 16 carbon atoms long, and this part of the fat molecule bulks so large compared to the glycerol part that the whole compound has properties somewhat like those of hydrocarbons such as petroleum or paraffin oils. The most important of these properties is insolubility in water. On the other hand, fats are very compact fuel molecules for the use of living organisms, because they yield more energy per unit weight than any other food. Carbohydrates, by contrast, are already partly oxidized. This is why fat rather than carbohydrate is stored for future nourishment in the fat cells of animals and in the seeds of plants.

The problem of digesting fats is not simply one of chemically breaking them down to fatty acids and glycerol; more important, it involves reduction in size of the droplets in which fats are found in aqueous solution. Since the contents of the stomach and intestine are watery mixtures, the insoluble fats tend to aggregate into drops as the food is fragmented and other materials are removed. Were it to remain in this form most of the fat would pass on through the digestive tract and be lost in the feces. For effective absorption from the intestine into the blood stream it is necessary that these fat droplets be reduced to the size range of colloidal particles such as the fats in milk—that is, to droplets one or a few micra in diameter. Fragmenting one millimeter drop into 10^9 droplets one micron in diameter increases by a thousandfold the surface area of fat exposed to the surrounding water. It is at the surface of the fat droplets that reactions occur by which fats are transported across the wall of the intestine.

Bile salts present in bile—which is the liquid that flows from the liver into the small intestine of vertebrates—have the property of spreading out into thin layers between fats and water. A molecule of a bile salt is attracted both to the fat and to the water; that is, it has two parts, one tending to make it water soluble and the other tending to make it soluble in fats or oils. In the presence of both fat and water these molecules tend to slip into interfaces between the two and hence increase the amount of such surface area.

Fats in the intestinal contents are also acted upon by enzymes manufactured in the pancreas, the large gland, mentioned above, that lies close to the intestine and secretes into it pancreatic juice containing several important substances. The fat-digesting enzymes called pancreatic lipases catalyze the breaking up of fats into the three fatty acids plus the glycerol to which they had been joined. Despite the availability of pancreatic lipases in the intestines of mammals, however, some of the emulsified fats penetrate through the layers of cells lining the intestine as complete fat molecules.

PROTEINS

The third major foodstuff consists of proteins, those unique *macromolecules* that are one of the major features of living protoplasm. As seen in *Cell Structure and Function*, these are polymers of amino acids; the digestion of protein food consists of the breaking down of proteins first into smaller polymers and finally to the amino acid units themselves. Twenty-two common amino acids make up most of the proteins found in animals and plants, and they differ considerably in size and complexity. Since all of them have an organic acid group (COOH) in close proximity to an amino group (NH_2), all amino acids are exactly alike in one part of the molecule—that is, $CHNH_2COOH$. This key portion of the amino acid molecule is attached to other groups that vary in size and chemical structure. For simplicity the individually different parts of the several amino acids are customarily abbreviated as R; thus in this shorthand, representation all of the biologically important amino acids forming proteins are symbolized as $RCHNH_2COOH$. When amino acids are joined together to form proteins the COOH and NH_2 groups on two different amino acids react as follows to form what is called a peptide bond between the carbon atom of one and the nitrogen of the other:

$$R_1-\underset{\underset{\displaystyle N}{|}}{\overset{\overset{\displaystyle H}{|}}{C}}-\overset{O}{\overset{\|}{C}}-OH \; + \; H-\underset{\underset{\displaystyle H}{|}}{\overset{\overset{\displaystyle H}{|}}{N}}-\underset{\underset{\displaystyle R_2}{|}}{C}-\overset{O}{\overset{\|}{C}}-OH \; \rightarrow$$

$$R_1-\underset{\underset{\displaystyle N}{|}}{\overset{\overset{\displaystyle H}{|}}{C}}-\overset{O}{\overset{\|}{C}}-\underset{\underset{\displaystyle H}{|}}{N}-\underset{\underset{\displaystyle R_2}{|}}{\overset{\overset{\displaystyle H}{|}}{C}}-\overset{O}{\overset{\|}{C}}-OH \; + \; H_2O$$

The product of this reaction, called a *dipeptide,* has many of the properties of a single amino acid; it can react in the same way with either the NH_2 or the COOH group of a third amino acid to form a *tripeptide,* and this process is in fact continued in the formation of proteins until hundreds of amino acids are linked by peptide bonds.

When proteins are consumed as food they are broken down into their component amino acids before being taken through the walls of the digestive tract. In the digestive systems of highly organized animals specialized enzymes are produced that attack the bonds between certain amino acids and not those between others. Some of these break long chains of proteins near the middle, others break off only terminal amino acids near the ends of the chains. Since some of the amino acids have additional COOH or NH_2 groups within the entity R, peptide bonds can link these amino acids to two others, and when this occurs the chain of amino acids becomes branched. Some digestive enzymes work at or close to such branching points. As a result of this diversity of enzymes for protein digestion, protein molecules are split into a variety of fragments that in turn are acted upon by other enzymes to complete the separation into single amino acids. In simpler animals these steps all occur within food vacuoles or in single chambers such as the gastrovascular cavity of coelenterates or the branched digestive tract of the Platyhelminthes. In more highly organized animals such as vertebrates or insects, however, different kinds of protein digestion occur at separate places along the "disassembly" line of the digestive system.

In the vertebrate animals, the first steps in protein digestion occur in the stomach, where the protein molecules are broken into various kinds and sizes of polypeptides, usually in acid solution. The protein digestive enzyme secreted by the gland cells of the stomach walls is called *pepsin*. Other glands secrete hydrochloric acid (HCl) to acidify the food in the stomach. In the small intestine, however, conditions become slightly alkaline as a result of the secretions of glands in the wall of the intestine. There, other protein-digesting enzymes complete the breakdown of proteins and peptides that have escaped the action of the pepsin. For the most part they are adapted to work on peptides and reduce them to single amino acids. Some of the intestinal protein-digesting enzymes also come from glands in the walls of the intestine, but the most important single one, called *trypsin,* is produced in the pancreas. In mammals the whole process of protein digestion is somewhat more rapid and efficient than in fishes, reptiles, or amphibians; one reason for this superiority is the greater acidity of the stomach combined with the greater division of labor among specialized protein-digesting enzymes.

PROTECTION AGAINST SELF-DIGESTION

The efficiency of protein-digesting enzymes raises an important problem: what prevents pepsin and trypsin from digesting the cells that produce them, or the lining of the stomach and intestine? If these same cells were part of the food, they would be rapidly destroyed, and their proteins broken up into single amino acids. Yet stomach, intestinal wall, and cells of the pancreas remain intact for years, all the while producing enough pepsin, trypsin, and other enzymes to digest the whole animal many times over. This is an example of the complexities of chemical engineering as it is carried out by living organisms: it is not sufficient simply to manufacture potent digestive enzymes; they must in addition be prevented from exercising their powers of protein breakdown until the appropriate time and place.

Pepsin and trypsin are not elaborated as such in the gland cells of stomach wall or pancreas; instead, these cells secrete inactive molecules, *pepsinogen* and *trypsinogen*. When these reach the acid stomach or the alkaline contents of the small intestine they lose a few amino acids on parts of the enzyme molecule, and this loss uncovers the active surface of the enzyme so that it can go to work catalyzing the separation of other proteins into their component amino acids. A little active pepsin or trypsin already present hastens this uncovering process, and the activation therefore proceeds at a rapid rate once the pepsinogen or the trypsinogen reaches the place where it is needed. Further protection is provided the cells that line the digestive tract by a layer of secreted mucus that forms an effective barrier against the active digestive enzymes.

THE ACTIVE NATURE OF INTESTINAL ABSORPTION

So far nothing has been said concerning the way in which food molecules move from the digestive cavity into the animal. Sometimes after a heavy meal there is a higher concentration of, for example, glucose in the intestine than in the blood that flows through capillaries in its wall, and in such cases glucose molecules diffuse from the region of high concentration to the place where they are less abundant. The end result of simple diffusion, however, would be an equal concentration of glucose in blood and intestinal contents, and this would leave much of this valuable substance available for the intestinal bacteria to use as fuel for their metabolism rather than that of the host animal. Actual measurements have shown that most of the time there is a higher concentration of glucose in the blood than in the contents of the intestine, but that this sugar nevertheless moves fairly rapidly into the blood—that is, *against the concentration gradient*. This is one of the clearest examples known in biology of the "uphill" flow of some molecule, an occurrence that is almost always to the advantage of the animal concerned. The movement of substances against a concentration gradient is one of the most important processes that distinguish living protoplasm from inert nonliving systems, and it is called *active transport*.

We would of course like to know how the active transport of glucose takes place, but as yet we can provide only partial explanations. A basic principle of physical chemistry states that if a given substance is equally concentrated, initially, in two adjacent containers (here the intestine and the blood vessels), work is required to separate the molecules of this substance into two portions, one of high and the other of lower concentration. Active transport thus requires energy, and in living systems it is accomplished only by cells that are utilizing more food and have a higher rate of activity than they would were they not engaged in active transport. Just how the energy of biochemical reactions is utilized to achieve active transport is not yet clearly understood, but the most widely held theories postulate some sort of carrier molecule that combines at one side of the cell with the glucose or other substance to be transported, and is separated at the other side of the cell by local enzymes or other (poorly understood) conditions there. It is quite possible that within the next few years much more will be learned about this universally important living process, and such knowledge will solve one of the most intriguing problems of biology.

SUGGESTED READING LIST

ANNISON, E. H., and LEWIS, D., 1959. *Metabolism in the rumen.* New York: Wiley.

PROSSER, C. L., and BROWN, F. A., JR., 1961. *Comparative animal physiology,* 2d ed. Philadelphia: Saunders. Chapters 4 and 5.

ROGERS, T. A., "The metabolism of ruminants, *Scientific American,* Feb. 1958, p. 34.

RUCH, T. C., and FULTON, J. F., 1960. *Textbook of physiology,* 18th ed. Philadelphia: Saunders. Chapters 42-47.

YAPP, W. B., 1960. *An introduction to animal physiology,* 2d ed. New York: Oxford University Press. Chapter 1.

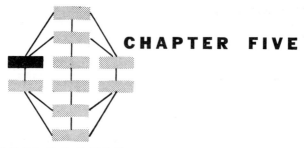

CHAPTER FIVE

METABOLISM

AND

RESPIRATION INTRODUCTION—Living organisms carry out

their intricate and balanced activities by a controlled release of energy from the oxidation of foodstuffs; the general term for this process is *metabolism*. *Metabolic rates* are expressed in units of energy released per unit time (equivalent to power)—for example, kilogram calories per hour. The process of bringing oxygen to the cells of an animal and carrying away carbon dioxide (CO_2) is quite as essential as the digestion and absorption of food. Water, like carbon dioxide, is a product of metabolism, and under some conditions the water formed by oxidation of food supplies the entire needs of animals that live in extremely dry situations. For example, some small desert mammals such as the kangaroo rat live for months without drinking water and eating only dry food. Although they lose water steadily through their urine and by evaporation from the skin and especially from the lungs, this loss is balanced by the so-called metabolic water from the oxidation of the hydrogen atoms in their food.

The exchange of oxygen and carbon dioxide between active cells and the outside environment is usually called *respiration* or *respiratory gas exchange,* since both oxygen and carbon dioxide are gases at ordinary temperatures. The organs for their exchange with the environment are called *respiratory systems.* The term "respiration" is also used for the biochemical events that occur inside living cells in the stepwise breakdown of food molecules and the transfer of the resulting energy to other molecules. This important activity is best called *cellular respiration.* Food molecules can be stored within the body of an animal, but only in special and limited cases (such as in diving animals) is oxygen stored against future need or carbon dioxide allowed to accumulate for future disposal. Respiratory gas exchange is a crucial and continuous process. The efficiency of this process, and the resistance of the respiratory system to failure under adverse conditions determine in large measure the success and survival of the animal in question.

Although oxygen and carbon dioxide are gases when exposed to air at ordinary temperatures, their biological roles are played in aqueous solution. Oxygen remains as O_2 whether it is in the gas phase or in solution, and only a relatively small amount can be dissolved in water. When exposed to air, which contains just under 21 percent O_2, approximately one milliliter (ml) of gaseous oxygen will dissolve in 100 milliliters of water in a near-freezing temperature; only about half as much is held in solution at the body temperatures of birds and mammals. Carbon dioxide, on the other hand, reacts with water chemically to form carbonic acid, H_2CO_3, which in turn dissociates rapidly to form H^+ and HCO_3^- ions. In water and tissue fluids that are neither strongly acid nor alkaline most of the carbon dioxide exists as bicarbonate ion rather than as dissolved CO_2 molecules. Because water reacts in this way with CO_2 it can hold much more carbon dioxide, as bicarbonate ion, than it can hold oxygen in solution.

RESPIRATORY EXCHANGE BY DIFFUSION AND CIRCULATION

Unicellular animals and others of small size have no special organs for respiration. The use of oxygen or the production of carbon dioxide by reactions occurring within their protoplasm sets up concentration gradients: oxygen becomes less concentrated inside the cell and carbon dioxide more so as a result of the oxidation of food molecules. Along such concentration gradients O_2 and CO_2 move by diffusion, and this simple physical process suffices for the needs of protoplasm that lies within a fraction of a millimeter of the surrounding water. Protoplasm cannot operate at too low a concentration of oxygen, and excessive amounts of CO_2 are injurious. Hence a reliance on diffusion as a means of transporting the respiratory gases sets a limit of roughly one millimeter to the thickness that can be attained by an unspecialized animal. The difficulty can be alleviated by lowering the metabolic rate, and hence the rate at which oxygen is consumed, but this in turn severely limits the activity of the animal and its ability to obtain food or escape from enemies. It is important to appreciate that this limitation applies not to total volume but only to the thickness—that is, the distance from the outside water to the deepest parts of the protoplasm that carry out an active metabolism. Inert skeletal material or the jellylike tissues that lie between the inner and outer cell layers coelenterates may be farther removed from the surface than muscle cells or nervous tissue.

Another important fact about diffusion as a means of respiratory exchange in small animals is that it suffices regardless of the complexity of the animal or the phylum to which it belongs, provided only that the animal's size is small and its surface permeable to O_2 and CO_2. Thus early stages in the development of complex animals, including ourselves, require no specialized respiratory organs. Most adult members of the phylum Arthropoda, for example, possess specialized gills and associated blood vessels to obtain oxygen from their environment, but very small arthropods, even though fully adult, often lack such respiratory structures altogether. All their respiratory exchange can easily take place through the skin.

The size limits set by diffusion of oxygen and carbon dioxide can be greatly extended if the protoplasm or other noncellular fluids are in motion. Over distances of more than about one millimeter, respiratory gases and other molecules can be stirred about and thus supplied where needed much more readily by circulation of fluid than by diffusion through stationary protoplasm. In simpler multicellular animals such as coelenterates it is the water within the digestive cavity or other internal cavities that serves this purpose. The branched digestive cavity of a flatworm and the body cavities of roundworms and annelid worms contain fluid that is circulated in a rather irregular fashion by the contractions of muscles in the body wall surrounding these cavities. Such internal circulation aids in respiratory gas transport, but a great improvement in efficiency occurs when it is supplemented, as it is in most of the annelid worms and in the phyla Mollusca, Arthropoda, and Chordata, by an organized circulatory system in which blood is pumped through more or less definite channels. Such circulatory systems will be considered in Chapter 7, but the functioning of respiratory and circulatory systems are so intimately interwoven that they must be studied with this interrelationship firmly in mind.

GILLS

A skin that allows free diffusion of oxygen and carbon dioxide cannot fail to be rather permeable to other small molecules as well. This poses less critical problems for marine animals, in which the body fluids are not greatly different from sea water, than for animals that live in fresh water, in the soil, or on land and must maintain their internal fluids in a very different state from the surrounding environment. The better the protection afforded by a specialized skin, the poorer the skin necessarily becomes as a surface for respiratory exchange. For example, no animal has developed a skin that permits free exchange of O_2 and CO_2 while remaining impermeable to water molecules. It is therefore not surprising to find that the more active types of animals, and those equipped with protective skins, have specialized portions of the body surface devoted specifically to respiratory exchange. The simplest of these are merely areas where the external surface is folded or formed into projecting appendages covered by a thin, permeable skin under which are located thin-walled blood vessels or spaces containing a fluid that can carry O_2 and CO_2 as it circulates within the animal's body. Typical examples can be found among the annelid worms, including those that secrete around their bodies a hard, protective tube—a sort of external skeleton or shell. This is impermeable to the respiratory gases, and many of these worms have fine, threadlike *gill filaments* that project outside of the tube from time to time and allow respiratory gas exchange with the blood that flows through them. Others have shorter appendages that serve as gills. Filamentous gills are especially prominent among some of the marine worms that live in muddy layers on the botton of the ocean where oxygen is often very scarce because of the activities of bacteria. In other cases such gills occur in worms that live in burrows in the mud or sand and do not secrete shells around their bodies. In all cases the gills are retracted into the tube or burrow when danger threatens or when the water becomes strongly agitated or absent, as at low tide. Among vertebrate animals some salamanders (class Amphibia) also have external gills, but they are of fairly minor importance because the moist skin and effective circulatory systems of these animals suffice for most of the respiratory gas exchange required for a relatively inactive life.

Gills that expose a large surface area must float loosely in sheltered water and are hence vulnerable to injury in an actively moving animal. In their place most of the larger and more active types of aquatic animals have gills located inside a cavity. These cavities always have openings to the outside water, and often there are means for circulating fresh water over the gills to facilitate respiratory exchange. The three major groups of highly organized aquatic animals possessing such protected gills are the phylum Mollusca, the class Crustacea of the phylum Arthropoda, and the fishes (class Pisces of the phylum Chordata). Although all three have gills that accomplish the same function, the particular arrangements are quite different.

In most of the mollusks the gills lie inside a *mantle cavity* into which also open the mouth and anus. (See Fig. 2-4.) In the clams and snails this cavity is inside the hard shell, and water is circulated through it mainly by the beating of millions of cilia. These are motile, hairlike structures similar to the cilia or flagellae of protozoans, but in mollusks they are parts of specialized cells covering the surface of the gills and sometimes other parts of the lining of the mantle cavity. In the more active squid and octopus the mantle cavity has thicker and more muscular walls that actively pump water in and out and thus ventilate the gills, which also lie within the mantle cavity. These mollusks have a circulatory system in which blood is pumped through the gills to carry oxygen and carbon dioxide to and from the rest of the body.

In the crayfish, lobster, crabs, and many smaller members of the class

Crustacea the gills are relatively large and lie on the two sides of the thorax or middle portion of the body lateral to the body proper but inside the main plates of the chitinous exoskeleton. (See Fig. 5-1.) As in the mollusks, the circulatory system pumps blood through the gills. Some crustacea have other types of gills attached to the jointed appendages, but the type illustrated diagrammatically in Fig. 5-1 is typical of the larger and more active members of this important group of animals.

Among the vertebrates, aquatic respiratory systems are most highly developed in the fishes. The gills are located on the edges of lateral openings from the pharynx, that part of the digestive system just posterior to the mouth. There are five or six of these openings, called *gill slits*, on each side of the pharynx. In the sharks and their relatives with cartilagenous skeletons the gill slits open directly to the outside. In most other fishes, however, designated by contrast bony fishes, the several gill slits open into two other chambers located laterally to the pharynx, one on each side. These in turn are covered by a plate of tissue usually stiffened with cartilage or bone, called the *operculum,* and at the posterior edge of the operculum is the gill opening that is an obvious external feature of the most familiar fish. Between adjacent gill slits on each side is located a gill arch to which the gill filaments are attached and through which they are supplied with blood vessels. Water is circulated from the mouth through the gill slits and out through the opercular cavity of bony fishes by two mechanisms. The opening and closing movements of the fish's mouth bring water into it, most of the water being then forced out over the gills because soft flaps of connective tissue around the mouth opening act as check valves preventing water from flow-

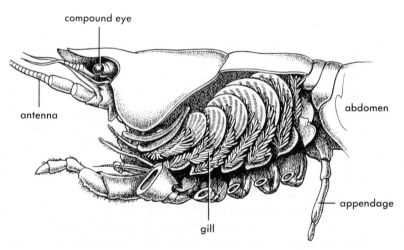

Fig. 5-1. The gills of a crayfish (Class Crustacea). The exoskeleton has been cut away to show the gills in relation to the remainder of the body. (After T. H. Huxley, *The Crayfish.* London, C. Kegan Paul, 1880.)

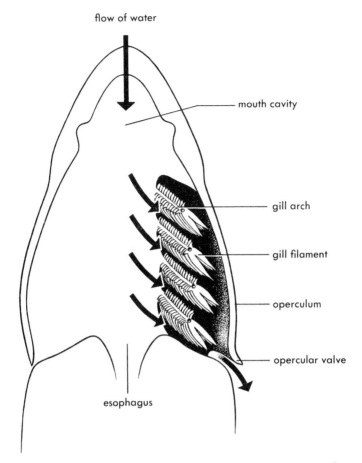

flow of water

mouth cavity

gill arch

gill filament

operculum

opercular valve

esophagus

Fig. 5-2. The mouth cavity and gills of a typical fish. The valve at the edge of the operculum prevents backflow as the operculum is moved outward; similar valves on the lips are not visible in this figure. In life, filaments from neighboring gill arches almost touch so that all water must pass very close to the surface of one or more gill filaments.

ing out of the mouth. Furthermore, the operculum is moved outward by muscles attached to its outer surface, and this enlargement of the opercular cavity draws water past the gills. While the mouth is being opened, another valvelike flap of tissue at the posterior edge of the operculum prevents water from flowing back into the opercular cavity. (See Fig. 5-2.) By either or both of these types of pumping action most fishes circulate water through the mouth and over the gills. In a few very active swimmers such as mackerel the movement of the fish through the water causes most of the current past the gills. Mackerel are thus active fish that do not stay still for long periods because in the absence of such ventilation of the gills they fail to obtain enough oxygen.

In the gills of fishes, and also in those of some of the mollusks, blood is carried close to the gill surface in the opposite direction to that in which the water is flowing. This countercurrent permits a more efficient exchange of oxygen between blood and water, because the blood that has already taken up some oxygen is exposed to fresh water with the highest concentration of dissolved oxygen just before it leaves the exposed surface of the gill.

RESPIRATORY SURFACES FOR AIR

Air contains about 21 percent oxygen, a contrast to the small amount that water can hold in solution—between 0.5 and 1 volume of gaseous oxygen per 100 volumes of water that has come into equilibrium with the atmosphere. Hence it would seem at first thought that animals living in air should have relatively simple respiratory problems. Such is not the case, for air is so different from protoplasm that terrestrial animals require thicker and less permeable skins that necessarily prevent any adequate diffusion of oxygen and carbon dioxide. Any living surface through which respiratory exchange can take place is also subject to the danger of water loss, whether it be a human lung or the moist body surface of a worm. Many small terrestrial animals do have moist skins and survive for extended periods only by remaining in places where the air is nearly or quite saturated with water vapor. But many vertebrates, the terrestrial arthropods, and some of the snails (phylum Mollusca) have respiratory systems that permit them to spend their whole lives in air that may be moist or dry.

The terrestrial snails are good examples of animals equipped with small mantle cavities that are called *diffusion lungs* because they are kept at a constant volume with very little active pumping of air in and out. The opening is rather restricted in size, and part of the inner surface has blood vessels close to the air. Since oxygen diffuses thousands of times more rapidly through air than through water or protoplasm, only rather large animals need to circulate the air within a hollow respiratory organ. Many diffusion lungs have the inner surface folded to increase its surface area. Water loss is reduced by the small size of the opening of a diffusion lung to the outside air, and the rapid diffusion of oxygen through air suffices to bring in all that is needed through the small opening.

TRACHEAL RESPIRATORY SYSTEMS

Insects and a few other arthropods have a highly specialized type of respiratory system that is an elaboration of the diffusion lung. In several of the body segments insects have paired openings called *spiracles,* one on each side of the body. These communicate with air-filled cavities from which extend small branching tubes called *tracheae* (sing. *trachea*). The branching is repeated over and over again until the terminal elements, called *tracheoles,* are often less than one micron in diameter. Except at their very ends the tracheae and tracheoles are filled with air, and they ramify to every part of the insect's body. The more active an organ or tissue, the more abundant are the tracheoles supplying it. In some cases tracheoles even penetrate between individual cells. (See Fig. 5-3.) Despite the small size of the tracheal tubes, oxygen and carbon dioxide travel along them by diffusion, although the larger air-filled cavities are ventilated by the movements of surrounding muscles or exoskeleton. The spiracles are closed and opened by valves that are in turn operated by minute muscles. Each spiracle also has hairs around its edges to prevent dust particles and parasites from entering.

This tracheal respiratory system of insects provides a direct avenue for respiratory exchange between the outside air and the cell where metabolic reactions take place. It is an efficient method, and in insects the blood is not needed for carrying oxygen and carbon dioxide. A tracheal respiratory system would probably not suffice for the needs of a large animal unless there were an extension of the ventilation, for even in air there are limits to the distance over which diffusion can carry enough oxygen along minute tubes to supply the extensive requirements of these most active animals. A flying insect in particular uses oxygen at a much higher rate, per gram of body weight, than any bird. Along with the need for renewing the exoskeleton by periodic molts, the fact that tracheal respiratory systems depend upon diffusion along the fine air-filled tubules may set limits to the size that insects can attain.

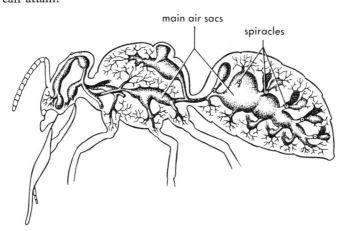

Fig. 5-3. The tracheal respiratory system of an insect; the smaller tracheae and tracheoles cannot be shown at this scale.

THE LUNGS OF FISHES, AMPHIBIANS, AND REPTILES

During the first hundred million years or more of its history our own phylum was composed exclusively of fishes. Only after vertebrates had become a highly successful aquatic group did terrestrial, air-breathing forms appear. Many fishes have air-filled chambers connected with the digestive system, and air is swallowed and forced into these cavities so that respiratory gas exchange can take place through their walls. Most fish possessing such air chambers, or air bladders as they are sometimes called, also have efficient gills, and they may use either or both types of respiratory system according to circumstances. One group, the lungfishes, have only lungs and must breathe by coming to the surface. This handicap is offset by their ability to survive long periods when the water has evaporated from the streams and pools in arid climates.

Amphibians usually have paired lungs connected with the pharynx through a type of muscular valve, the *larynx*, that prevents water from entering the single tube called the trachea that conveys air towards the lungs. The trachea branches into two *bronchi*, one leading to each of the lungs. Amphibian lungs are fairly simple sacks with only a moderate folding of the inner surface to increase the area for exchange of oxygen and carbon dioxide with the rich supply of small blood vessels lining the lungs. The lungs do not contain muscles to pump air in and out; this is accomplished by squeezing of the muscles of the body wall or sometimes by a modified swallowing motion that forces air into the lungs. Reptiles have similar lungs, but they are often more highly convoluted on their inner surfaces.

MAMMALIAN LUNGS

In mammals the lungs are larger and so highly honeycombed with branching air passages and folded walls that there are no large uninterrupted volumes of free air. Instead, the air is confined to small chambers known as alveoli, roughly 1 millimeter in diameter, each located at the end of a terminal branch of one of the bronchi. The lungs of a mammal lie in a *pleural cavity*, which is bounded by the "cage" formed by the ribs and the layers of muscle and connective tissue spread between them. The posterior edge of the pleural cavity is formed by a sheet of muscle and connective tissue called the *diaphragm*. The lungs are not attached to the walls of the pleural cavity, except where the bronchi enter; because of a slight elasticity of the connective tissue surrounding each alveolus a mammalian lung collapses if removed from this cavity. The only reason this does not happen during the life of the mammal is that the pressure is slightly lower inside the pleural cavity surrounding the lung than in the outside air. If the cavity is opened, the lung collapses; when this occurs on both sides, the respiratory system is crippled and death ensues rapidly. (See Fig. 5-4.)

The ventilation of mammalian lungs is accomplished through the contractions of muscles that raise and lower the ribs relative to the sternum, thus changing the volume of the pleural cavity in chest breathing. In addition, the contraction of the diaphragm also pumps air in and out of the

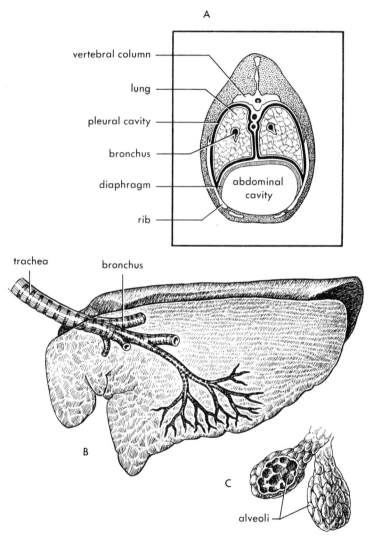

Fig. 5-4. The pleural cavity and lungs of a mammal: (A) Cross section showing the lungs in the pleural cavity; (B) Structure of one lung in greater detail; (C) Enlarged view of a few alveoli, the walls of which contain thin-walled capillaries.

lungs. It is not clear why mammalian lungs should lie loosely in a partially evacuated pleural cavity; perhaps the constant expansion and contraction of the cavity causes less abrasive wear of the delicate lung tissue than would be the case in some other arrangement.

THE LUNGS OF BIRDS

The power of flight has required of birds many highly efficient mechanisms within their bodies, and the respiratory system is almost as highly adapted for flying as are the appendages. The lungs are firmly attached to the body wall and arranged in such a fashion that the movements of the wings pump air in and out. In addition to the lungs, birds have an elaborate system of air sacs. These are connected with the trachea by large tubes that pass directly through the lungs, though other tubes branch and supply air to small cavities lined with blood vessels, much as in the alveoli of mammals. In the bird lung, air passes over vascular surfaces both during inspiration and expiration. On inspiration, part of the air passes through the lungs into a pair of large *abdominal air sacs* and then back out on expiration. The net effect of this complex system is that during a large fraction of the respiratory cycle fresh air is moved over vascular surfaces where the blood can exchange O_2 and CO_2 with air. Thin-walled tubes and other air sacs ramify into many parts of a bird's body, even into many of the bones, as mentioned in Chapter 3. The air sacs are not themselves sufficiently well supplied with small blood vessels to serve as surfaces for respiratory exchange with the blood, nor are their inner surfaces folded to increase surface area; they are clearly accessory structures that improve the functioning of the avian respiratory system, although their detailed workings have never been carefully investigated. They may serve to remind us of two facts: (1) mammalian organs are not necessarily the most efficient to be found in the various animals that exist, and (2) many refined physiological mechanisms in the bodies of animals still await adequate study and analysis of their function.

METABOLIC RATES AND FACTORS THAT AFFECT THEM

Since metabolic rates reflect the general activity of the animal in question, sluggish and quiescent animals have lower rates than very active ones. Coelenterates, for instance, have relatively low rates of oxygen consumption, whereas mammals and insects have much higher rates of energy release. Vigorous muscular work involves several times the oxygen consumption necessary when the same animal is quiet. Depending upon its size, a mammal running at top speed uses some 5 to 20 times as much oxygen per minute as it does when resting quietly. Flying insects may have metabolic rates as much as 100 times the resting rate.

Larger animals of course use more energy than smaller ones of the same type, but the metabolic rate per gram of living tissue varies in just the opposite manner. For example, the rate of oxygen consumption per gram of body weight is much smaller for an elephant than for a mouse. There is no clear explanation for this effect, although it used to be thought that metabolic rate was proportional to surface area. Since surface area is proportional to the square of the body length, the surface area varies as the ⅔ power of the weight. The metabolic rate, however, varies among mammals, crustaceans, and fish not as the ⅔ power of weight, but as a somewhat higher power, approximately 0.7 to 0.75. On the other hand, animals below about 1 millimeter in size usually have a metabolic rate approximately proportional to the weight; that is, the intrinsic rate per gram of tissue is nearly constant. This is also the approximate size above which diffusion is insufficient to supply oxygen to active tissues, a fact that suggests that the smaller intrinsic metabolic rate in larger animals may be due to the problem of providing adequate circulatory and respiratory systems to supply the tissues that are some distance from the respiratory surfaces.

The temperature of the animal's body also has an important effect on metabolic rate, which roughly doubles with every 10-degree-Centigrade increase in temperature within the limits that the animal can tolerate. Most animals remain nearly at the same temperature as the air or water in which they live. They are called by biologists *poikilothermic* rather than "cold blooded," because some of them may have quite a high temperature when in warm air or water. Birds and mammals are exceptions, and are popularly called "warm blooded." The important distinction, however, is not the warmth but the *regulation* of their body temperature—the ability to hold it close to a constant value despite fluctuations in the surrounding temperature. Hence the biological term for birds and mammals is *homothermic*, meaning constant in temperature. In the hot desert sun the poikilothermic lizard may have a higher body temperature than the homothermic camel.

The metabolic rate of poikilothermic animals falls rather rapidly with decreasing temperature, approximately to half its previous value for a temperature drop of 10 degrees C. Homothermic animals must react metabolically in just the opposite manner. When exposed to cold air or water they must generate more heat to hold the normal temperature of their own tissues. Their oxygen consumption does increase at lower temperatures, though the need for added heat production is often offset by increasing the thickness, and hence the thermal insulation, of the fur or feathers.

Several kinds of mammals and a few species of birds exhibit an intermediate metabolic state in which they sometimes allow their body temperature to fall to that of the surrounding air for varying time periods. This is usually called *hibernation,* although it may occur at other seasons than winter, and it serves to reduce considerably the animal's metabolic rate and hence its consumption of food. Hibernation or a functionally similar state usually occurs when food is scarce and when an animal is utilizing reserves of fat stored within its body. At a reduced body temperature the lowered metabolic rate conserves these stores and permits survival over a longer period of hard times.

ANAEROBIC METABOLISM

Important exceptions are found to the general rule that oxygen is required for all animal metabolism, for there are animals that live in environments where oxygen is virtually absent. Often mud contains a sufficiently dense population of bacteria to use up all the oxygen; another environment almost devoid of oxygen is the intestinal tract of mammals. Some of the nematodes living in the intestines of mammals obtain energy from fats and carbohydrates by breaking them down only part way, and they give off as waste products substances such as lactic acid ($CH_3CHOHCOOH$), which in most animals would be oxidized further to CO_2 and water.

The partial breakdown of carbohydrates by the anaerobic nematodes is quite similar to the first steps in the breakdown of glucose in animals that do require oxygen, and it is called *glycolysis.* In many cells glycolysis can proceed at a faster rate than the subsequent steps leading to complete utilization of the energy available in glucose. For example, muscle cells often work at a greater rate than that corresponding to their rate of oxygen consumption, and lactic acid accumulates under these conditions. At the end of the period of strenuous exercise the muscle uses more oxygen than it would otherwise require. This is called "paying off the oxygen debt," and athletes will recognize it as the heavy breathing that follows immediately after a period of maximum exertion. During this time the accumulated lactic acid passes through the later steps in the sequence of cellular metabolic reactions that were previously blocked by the inadequate supply of oxygen.

Many microorganisms obtain much or all of their metabolic energy from glycolysis or similar methods of partially breaking down food molecules without any O_2. In fact, there is good reason to believe that the earliest living organisms were limited to this type of metabolism by the virtual absence of free oxygen in the earth's atmosphere. Only later, when green plants had produced vast quantities of O_2 as a by-product of photosynthesis, is it believed that fully aerobic metabolism became commonplace in animal cells. The much greater amount of energy obtainable from each molecule of food has long since made complete oxidation to CO_2 and water the most advantageous, and hence the most widespread, type of animal metabolism.

SUGGESTED READING LIST

Hock, R. J., and Covino, B. G., "Hypothermia," *Scientific American*, March 1958, p. 104.

Krogh, A., 1959. *Comparative physiology of respiratory mechanisms*. Philadelphia: University of Pennsylvania Press.

Lyman, C. P., and Chatfield, P. O., "Hibernation," *Scientific American*, Dec. 1950, p. 18.

Pearson, O. P., "The metabolism of humming birds," *Scientific American*, Jan. 1955, p. 69.

Prosser, C. L., and Brown, F. A., Jr., 1961. *Comparative animal physiology*, 2d ed. Philadelphia: Saunders. Chapters 7-9.

Ruch, T. C., and Fulton, J. F., 1960. *A textbook of physiology*, 18th ed. Philadelphia: Saunders. Chapters 48-50.

Welty, C., "Birds as flying machines," *Scientific American*, Mar. 1955, p. 88.

Wigglesworth, V. B., 1953. *Principles of insect physiology*, 5th ed. London: Methuen. Chapters 9, 13 and 14.

Williams, C. M., "Insect breathing," *Scientific American*, Feb. 1953, p. 28.

Winslow, C-E. A., and Herrington, L. P., 1949 *Temperature and human Life*. Princeton, N. J., Princeton University Press.

CHAPTER SIX

MOTILITY

AND

CONTRACTILE

TISSUES

INTRODUCTION—Protoplasm is seldom static. In some cells a semiliquid cytoplasm can be seen to flow, usually in a rough circuit, in such a way that a given particle is eventually carried back by this *protoplasmic streaming* to its starting place. An especially interesting type of intracellular motion is that of an amoeba or the amoebocytes of multicellular animals, in which lobes or strands of protoplasm are pushed out and retracted; this movement is explained at length in *Cell Structure and Function* in this series. Since even isolated pieces of amoeba cytoplasm show protoplasmic streaming, it is clear that this movement does not require the presence of an intact cell wall. Time-lapse motion pictures of living cells, in which one photograph is taken every several seconds or minutes and the film projected at 16 frames per second, show that the shapes of cells vary irregularly and that even the positions of major components such as the nucleus and mitochondria move about within the cytoplasm. On the other hand, most cells contain more fixed structure and undergo less internal movement. Almost all cells contain elongated protein molecules that shorten at times to constrict parts of the cell, especially its surfaces. Metabolic energy is used in these contractions, and much the same biochemical processes are involved in the mild, slow, and occasional contortions of connective tissue cells as in the rapid and forceful shortening of highly specialized muscle cells. In all cases the energy to power the movement comes originally from the oxidation of food molecules, and in most cases adenosine triphosphate (ATP) is an intermediate vehicle for energizing the shortening of contractile protein molecules.

Another important type of cellular motion is the beating of hairlike cilia or flagellae that project from the surfaces of many microorganisms as well as from cells forming the internal or external surfaces of many multicellular animals. Where they are external, the cilia may move the whole animal, as in some flatworms and the larvae of many invertebrate animals. More common, however, are ciliated internal surfaces over which water currents are set up by the coordinated beating of thousands of individual cilia. These vary from the currents that flow over the gills of clams to bring water to the respiratory surfaces and food to the mouth, to the cilia that line our own tracheae or windpipes to move a current of mucus upward toward the mouth and thus carry away from the lungs particles of dust and foreign matter. The structure and function of cilia are described in *Cell Structure and Function* and *Microbial Life* of this series.

THE STRUCTURE OF MUSCLE CELLS

In multicellular animals movement is one of the major body functions most likely to exhibit division of labor between specialized cells. In coelenterates as well as more highly organized animals some cells have a much higher concentration of contractile protein fibrils, which are called muscle cells. Usually they are elongated and their ends are attached in some fashion to the surrounding tissues so that their shortening pulls on other parts of the animal. In such highly organized animals as arthropods, mollusks, and vertebrates the muscle cells may become packed with the contractile protein complex called *actomyosin*. The structure of muscle cells varies widely from one type of animal to another, and in the different organs of a single complex animal. The simplest are elongated, spindle-shaped cells with the contractile protein mainly oriented parallel to the axis of the cell but not readily distinguishable from the rest of the cytoplasm by ordinary microscopic examination. This simple type of muscle cell makes up what is called the *smooth* muscle of vertebrates.

In many highly organized animals muscle cells form a syncytium, where a considerable volume of protoplasm is contained within a single cell membrane, with many nuclei located at intervals throughout the cytoplasm. Such a syncytial unit is called a *muscle fiber*, and it usually achieves more rapid or vigorous contractions than smooth muscle cells. In some cases, but by no means all, the actomyosin is organized on the macromolecular level so that elements of the molecular structure are regularly spaced throughout the syncytium. This arrangement produces under the light microscope a series of regular cross striations, and as a result these are called striated muscles. Most of the muscles of vertebrate animals are of this type, including those that are attached to the various parts of the skeleton and move them relative to one another. Hence striated muscle is often called, with reference to vertebrate animals, *skeletal muscle.* Many invertebrates, including even some coelenterates, also contain some striated muscle. In general, striated muscles contract rapidly and vigorously. The hearts of vertebrate animals consist of a special type of striated muscle, called *cardiac muscle,* which is a series of branching and interconnected muscle fibers, with only thin transverse partitions representing the walls of individual cells. (See Fig. 6-1.)

The organization of the actomyosin in striated muscle has recently been revealed by the combined use of the electron microscope and selective biochemical analysis of the different elements in the striated muscle fiber. The typical ultrastructure of a striated muscle is shown diagrammatically in Fig. 6-2; the identity of the molecular components has been established by first extracting samples of muscle with reagents known to remove selectively

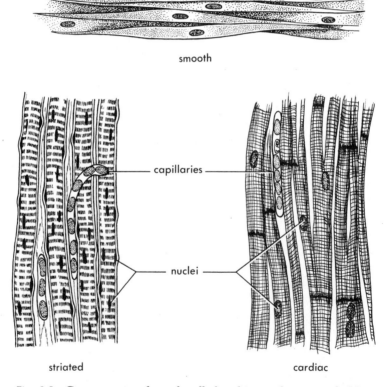

smooth

capillaries

nuclei

striated   cardiac

Fig. 6-1. Common types of muscle cells found in vertebrate animals. Note that smooth muscle consists of separate cells, whereas striated muscle is made up of fibers, each of which is a syncytium containing many nuclei. Cardiac muscle is divided into separate cells, but the cell walls are so thin as to be almost invisible in the light microscope. A capillary containing red blood cells is located close to the muscle cells.

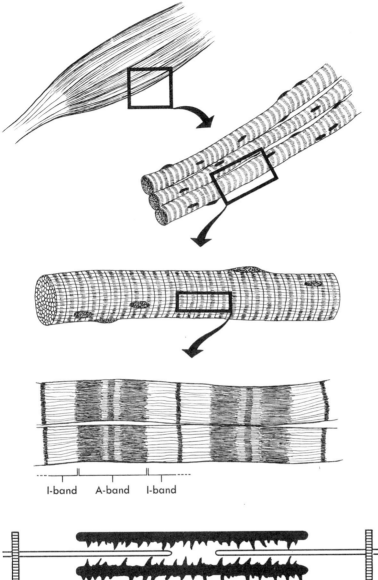

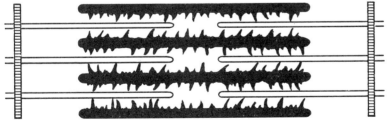

I-band   A-band   I-band

Fig. 6-2. Striated muscle shown diagrammatically at successively higher magnification. Note that the fibers contain many nuclei, which are located close to the fiber membrane. The A-band contains most of the myosin, while the long filaments of actin are believed to slide past the thicker myosin filaments as the muscle contracts and relaxes. The forces that cause the sliding motion are not known, but they may involve the projections from the fibers that are only barely resolved even by the best electron microscopes.

the actin or the myosin and then making electron microscope preparations that show the absence of the material so removed.

FUNCTIONAL SPECIALIZATIONS OF MUSCLE CELLS

Muscles are called upon to perform a variety of mechanical movements and to produce various kinds of forces over shorter or longer periods of time. They are also elastic structures, quite apart from their contractile function, and they have some of the properties of a sheet of rubber. Some muscles have a resting length that they exhibit when left alone, but if stretched they resist by an elastic force that increases as they are pulled out to longer lengths. Part of this elastic quality resides in the cell membranes or thin sheets of elastic connective tissue surrounding bundles of parallel muscle fibers. But many smooth muscles exhibit different resting lengths from time to time.

One of the specialized types of muscle is found in cases where the animal requires a steady tension subject to only gradual change. A typical example is the muscle that holds a clam's shell closed for hours when the animal is subjected to danger or adverse conditions. In many animals, including the vertebrates, there are hollow organs such as the intestinal tract and arteries that function best if their walls are held under a steady constrictive tension; this, however, must be varied from time to time according to the animal's changing needs and activities. Elastic connective tissue would suffice except for the requirement that the size of the hollow vessels must be variable. In these situations smooth muscle cells are arranged in layers, and their slow but steady contractions serve to keep up the steady tension required. In vertebrate animals smooth muscle is found, among other places, in the walls of the digestive tract, the blood vessels (except the heart), and the urinary bladder. In mammals tiny muscles of this type are arranged just below the skin to pull on the bases of the hairs and raise them in order to increase the thickness of the fur. Muscles that maintain such a steady tension are called *tonic* muscles, and the state of sustained constrictive tension is called *muscle tone.*

At quite another extreme of muscle function are the striated skeletal muscle fibers. One of their main functions is to move the animal quickly, or to produce rapid movements of its limbs. Striated muscles can and do contract within a fraction of a second after being excited by the motor nerves that supply them. They can also relax quickly so as to permit rapid oscillatory movements when these are needed, and their alternate contraction and relaxation lead to coordinated movements such as swimming, running, or flying. The wings of small birds and those of insects are moved back and forth many times per second.

Striated muscle fibers usually contract in a unitary fashion, following what is sometimes called the *"all-or-nothing"* principle. Unlike typical smooth muscles, these fibers either exhibit the full contraction of which they are capable under the prevailing conditions or else do not contract at all. This all-or-nothing reaction stems not from any impossibility of graded or partial shortening of the actomyosin, but from the arrangements within the syncytial fiber that assure a total activation each time the nerve cell stimulates the fiber.

Cardiac muscle must contract and relax rhythmically to pump blood through the heart. Since vertebrate animals are especially dependent on a continuous circulation to supply their cells with oxygen, heart muscle must alternate contraction with relaxation without pause for any appreciable period during the entire lifespan of the animal. Cardiac muscle, and also some types of smooth muscle, have the property of being intrinsically rhythmic. Even an isolated piece of heart muscle will spontaneously contract and relax at intervals. Furthermore, it is important that the contractions of heart muscle be so timed as to pump blood smoothly through the chambers of the heart. The structure of vertebrate heart muscle is one of branching and interconnected fibers, otherwise much like those of striated muscles. In a functional sense the heart behaves as a unit, and the contraction of a heart or one of its single chambers is ordinarily all-or-nothing. Like the single fiber of striated muscle, when a heart contracts it does so fully, producing as much contractile force as it can under the given conditions. Although cardiac muscle consists of a series of separate cells, separated by cell membranes visible under the electron microscope (though not evident under the light microscope, because of their extreme thinness), the spreading wave of contraction is not stopped or even appreciably slowed by these membranes.

THE ORGANIZATION OF MUSCLES

Whole animals do not move about by the activities of disorganized clumps of muscle cells, and a whole muscle is itself a harmonious community of contractile units—whether these be smooth muscle cells, striated muscle fibers, or the branching syncytium of cardiac muscle—surrounded by thin but tough sheets of connective tissue. In one of the simplest arrangements the axes of all the cells or fibers are parallel so that they all pull in the same direction. In many muscles, however, the need is not for a simple pull in a single direction, but for parts of a large muscle to pull in slightly different directions or to develop a greater force over part of its area. Many muscles are called upon to develop tension but not to contract over any great distance, and often their fibers are arranged at a considerable angle to the direction of pull, so that as they shorten and thicken the whole muscle shortens by a smaller distance but with a greater force than would be developed if all fibers were parallel to the direction of shortening.

Nor do muscles operate singly; almost every action of an animal involves at least two muscles working in a coordinated fashion. The simplest, most widespread, and most important structural arrangement for the coordination of muscle action is a pair of *opposed muscles*. Indeed it is difficult to find a skeletal muscle that is not matched by one pulling in the opposite direction. Every joint of each appendage of a vertebrate or an arthropod is bent or flexed by a *flexor muscle,* and is also straightened or extended by an *extensor muscle.* One can easily feel in his own arms and legs the stiffening of the opposed flexor and extensor muscles of the knee or elbow as these joints are flexed or extended. (See Fig. 6-3.)

In a few cases elastic connective tissue may pull in one direction and

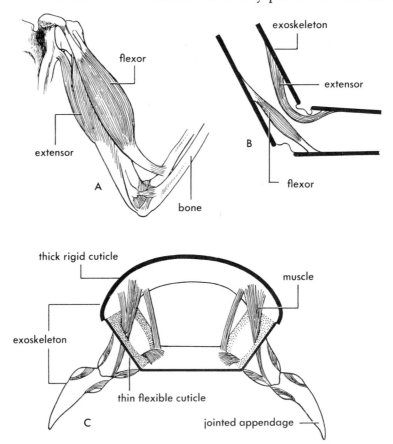

Fig. 6-3. Typical arrangements of opposed muscles controlling the joints (A) in the bony, internal skeleton of a vertebrate animal; (B and C) in the exoskeleton of an arthropod.

this force be opposed by a muscle. For example, the lens of the mammalian eye is enclosed in a capsule of elastic connective tissue that if unopposed would hold the lens in a more nearly spherical shape than it actually exhibits. The opposing force is applied by a ring of smooth muscle, the *ciliary muscle,* that pulls the capsule outward from all sides. By varying the strength of this contraction the animal can pull the elastic capsule into different shapes and thus focus the eye for objects lying at varying distances.

In many animals the body wall, the intestinal tract, or other hollow, tubular vessels contain two layers of muscle; in vertebrate animals these are usually smooth muscle cells. One set is arranged in a circular fashion so that its contraction squeezes or constricts the vessel, while another set is arranged longitudinally at right angles to the circular muscles—that is, parallel to the axis of the tube. When these longitudinal muscles contract, the tubular organ shortens and thickens. This arrangement is found in the cylindrical body wall of coelenterates, the body walls of roundworms and annelid worms, and in the intestinal tracts of all highly organized animals. The alternating and coordinated contractions of such circular and longitudinal muscles change the shape of these tubular cavities in a variety of ways. Often a wave of contraction of the circular muscles proceeds progressively along the tube, and this process, known as *peristalsis,* forces the contents in one direction. A special type of circular muscle is a sphincter, which closes off a tubular organ; an example is the anal sphincter at the posterior end of the intestinal tract.

Opposed muscles are stimulated by the nervous system in a coordinated fashion, so that when one contracts, the other partially relaxes. Hence the opposition is not a disorganized or competitive one, but a coordinated reciprocal arrangement whereby both members of the pair maintain a reasonable tension on the joint; while one relaxes, the other shortens to move the joint.

There are other muscles having complex arrangements of individual fibers or groups of fibers. The human tongue is a familiar example, and another case is the foot of mollusks such as clams and snails. Both organs consist of muscle and connective tissue that can assume a great variety of shapes by selective contraction of fibers oriented in several different directions and separately innervated.

THE ACTIVATION OF MUSCLE CELLS

The nature and functioning of nervous systems will be considered in Chapter 9, but at this point it is important to realize when studying muscles that motor nerve cells or *motor neurons* stimulate muscle cells to cause them to contract. Each of these highly elongated cells of the nervous system conveys unitary *nerve impulses* to a group of striated muscle cells called a *motor unit*. Nerve impulses may reach the motor unit at rates up to a few hundred per second. Most muscles contract more vigorously when excited by a rapid series of nerve impulses than they do in response to a single stimulus. This is particularly true when the stimulating nerve impulses arrive at a sufficiently high rate that the muscle cannot relax completely between successive stimuli. Under these conditions there results a sustained contraction of greater magnitude than the single response to one stimulus. Striated muscle fibers are well adapted to contract and relax quickly. Of course animals do not move by a series of twitches and convulsions; in most cases skeletal muscles contract only partly, because only some of the motor units are active and hence the muscle develops less than the maximum tension of which it is capable. By such sustained, partial contractions many sets of opposed muscles maintain a steady tonic contraction to hold the animal in any position other than complete relaxation.

SUGGESTED READING LIST

DAVSON, H., 1959. *A textbook of general physiology*, 2d ed. London: Churchill. Chapters 18-21.

HOCKING, B., "Insect flight," *Scientific American*, Dec. 1958, p. 92.

HOYLE, G., 1957. *Comparative physiology of the nervous control of muscular contraction*. Cambridge, Eng.: Cambridge University Press.

HUXLEY, H. E., "The contraction of muscle," *Scientific American*, Nov. 1958, p. 66.

PROSSER, C. L., and BROWN, F. A., JR., 1961. *Comparative animal physiology*, 2d ed. Philadelphia: Saunders. Chapters 14-17.

ROMER, A. S., 1949. *The vertebrate body*. Philadelphia: Saunders. Chapter 9.

WEIS-FOGH, T., "The flight of locusts," *Scientific American*, Mar. 1956, p. 116.

CHAPTER SEVEN

CIRCULATORY

SYSTEMS

INTRODUCTION—The importance of internal circulation for an animal of any considerable size has already been emphasized in Chapters 2 and 5. Protoplasmic streaming provides a sort of circulation within many single cells, and in coelenterates the contractions of the body wall redistribute the water contained within the digestive cavity. The need for oxygen in order to make efficient use of food molecules has led to the presence in most of the more highly organized animals not only of respiratory organs but of efficient arrangements for respiratory gas transport via the blood. It is the circulatory system that very often limits the activities and effectiveness of larger animals, including ourselves, and its failure is probably the most common immediate cause of death in human beings. The price of large size and an active life is a basic dependence on our circulatory system.

The fluid that flows in the circulatory systems of animals is basically a salt solution not greatly different in the proportions of the various ions from that of protoplasm. In this are dissolved or suspended macromolecules such as proteins, and usually a variety of blood cells. In all vertebrates the most common of these are the red blood cells, or *erythrocytes,* which are packed with the red protein called hemoglobin. The hemoglobins of various animals differ slightly, some of these differences being related to the animal's way of life. Blood also contains amoeboid cells of various types, as a group often called white blood cells, or *leucocytes.* There are many other proteins in addition to the hemoglobin: some of these form blood clots when exposed to air, others, called antibodies, combine with foreign proteins and remove them; and still others are hormones serving as chemical messengers that coordinate the functions of different parts of the animal's body. Occasionally there may be parasitic organisms living in the blood. Although one of the primary functions of blood in most animals is to aid in respiratory gas exchange, many other substances such as fat droplets and food molecules are also transported and exchanged via the blood between different parts of the body.

THE STRUCTURE OF CIRCULATORY SYSTEMS

Among the annelid worms, many have excellent circulatory systems that display all the major features found in more elaborate animals, though others have much simpler ones or none at all. Hence these animals provide examples of all major features of circulatory systems in general. The most striking difference between the circulatory system shown in Fig. 7-1 and those of vertebrates is the presence of several hearts or muscular thickenings of the walls of the larger blood vessels. Many of the larger vessels undergo peristaltic waves of contraction, much like those that occur in the intestinal tract.

The larger vessels with muscular walls are called *arteries;* in annelids there is often no sharp division between the thicker arteries and the several hearts. The larger arteries branch into successively smaller ones with thinner and less muscular walls. The limit of this latter process is reached in a type of blood vessel called the *capillary,* which has walls only one cell thick; often the cells are flattened so that less than a micron of protoplasm separates the blood from the outside of the capillary. Most molecules can easily diffuse through the walls of capillaries, and amoeboid cells circulating in the blood often push their way between the cells forming capillary walls and thus enter or leave the circulatory system proper. For a photomicrograph of a typical capillary, see Fig. 3-4.

The individual capillaries are usually a fraction of a millimeter in

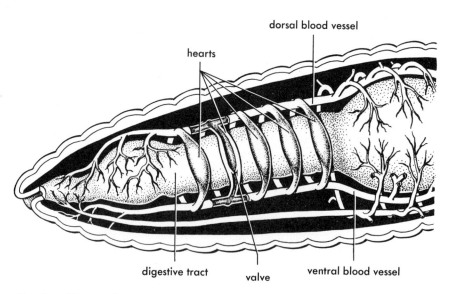

Fig. 7-1. The circulatory system of an annelid worm. Capillaries connect many of the grossly visible blood vessels, but cannot be shown at this scale.

length and connect to larger vessels called *veins,* which become larger as they proceed and receive blood from connecting capillaries and other small veins. The larger veins connect with the arteries and hearts; hence the blood flows around a circuit or, rather, may flow around any of a number of circuits depending upon which branch a given element of blood takes at the several branches of the arteries and capillaries.

In addition to this type of *closed circulation* that carries blood from a heart around through capillaries and back to the same or a different heart, some arteries of some annelids discharge blood into *sinuses,* or irregular spaces between cells, rather than connecting with capillaries. There are also some veins that have openings into which blood flows from the sinuses. Thus in one animal there may be both closed and *open circulation,* in which blood follows no clearly defined pathway. In groups of animals in which one type greatly predominates, the circulatory system as a whole is called by that name; for example, mollusks and arthropods have an open circulatory system, whereas vertebrates have a closed one.

The strongest muscular heart will not move blood around a circulatory system unless there are check valves to prevent back flow. All hearts are provided with effective valves, without which they would be useless. Less obvious, but almost equally important for an effective circulation are valves located in the veins (see Fig. 7-2). Here the pumping action of the hearts is ineffective owing to the relatively large and diffuse sinuses, but the alternate contractions of muscles in the body wall serve to move blood back to-

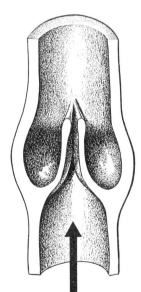

Fig. 7-2. A typical valve in a vein of a vertebrate animal, preventing back flow of blood away from the heart.

flow of blood

ward the hearts even though these muscles are not parts of the circulatory system proper. By their intermittent squeezing of the veins, blood is moved in the direction permitted by the check valves. In this way blood is moved out of open parts of a circulatory system, less rapidly than through the closed portions, but more effectively in one sense, because it can flow into immediate contact with cells rather than being separated from them even by the thin walls of a capillary. It is also possible in an open system for the blood to flow anywhere between cells instead of being limited to the locations of the capillaries.

In the mollusks and arthropods the circulatory system is usually less elaborate than in many of the annelid worms. From the heart a few arteries lead to major organs of the body, but large parts of the course followed by the blood lie outside of definite blood vessels, so that these circulatory systems are open ones. In squids there is a separate heart to pump blood through the gills. In many of these animals there are often no veins leading directly into the heart; instead, the heart is located in a large blood sinus that connects with others from all parts of the animal's body. Blood re-enters the heart through lateral openings called *ostia*, which are provided with check valves. As the heart contracts it forces blood into the arteries, and the valves close; on relaxation of the heart the natural elasticity of the muscle and connective tissue in its walls causes the internal volume to increase, and the valves open and blood flows in from the surrounding blood sinus. There are also valves at the entrance to the arteries to aid in the unidirectional flow of blood. Furthermore, many of the sinuses are fairly definite channels that lead from one diffuse space to another; thus in effect there are venous channels in the body to aid in the return of blood to the sinus surrounding the heart.

FUNCTIONAL ADAPTATIONS IN THE CIRCULATORY SYSTEMS OF VERTEBRATE ANIMALS

In all vertebrate animals the blood is retained in distinct vessels, with a few exceptions noted below. More important a point, however, is the high degree of specialization of the various parts of the system and its efficiency for the rapid transportation of blood to every part of the animal's body. This specialization has been necessitated by the large size and high degree of activity of vertebrates, our only rivals in the latter respect being the insects, in which the tracheal system replaces the blood for respiratory gas transport. The effectiveness of a circulatory system in rapid transport of blood can be measured in terms of the maximum hydrostatic pressure produced by the pumping action of the heart. Since this pressure is most easily measured in the larger arteries, it is usually known as the *arterial pressure.* In popular and medical usage it is often called simply "blood pressure," a term that on closer thought proves quite misleading since the pressure of the blood varies widely in different parts of the circulatory system. In typical animals of various major phyla the maximum arterial pressure, just after each heart beat, has the following approximate values when the animal is at rest (during exercise the arterial pressure rises somewhat, but seldom does it as much as double): annelids and arthropods, 5 to 10 mm Hg; active fish such as the salmon, 75 mm Hg in the ventral aorta before the gills, and 50 mm Hg in the dorsal aorta after the gills have been passed; birds and mammals 120 to 180 mm Hg. The much higher arterial pressure of birds and mammals varies rather little between large and small varieties.

An important aspect of vertebrate circulatory systems is the elasticity of the walls of the arteries, which is produced by the intrinsic elasticity of the circular smooth muscle cells and also by the presence of a large amount of elastic connective tissue. The high arterial pressure stretches the artery walls much as rubber tubing can be stretched by water pressure. This stretching in turn creates a small reservoir of blood under moderate pressure that can be forced through the smaller, branching arteries and the capillaries. Although the arterial pressure rises sharply at each heart beat to cause the pulse, it also remains quite high throughout the cardiac cycle. The walls of the smallest terminal arteries, called *arterioles,* have relatively more smooth muscles than the larger arteries. These muscles contract to reduce the flow of blood through arterioles, and this is the basic mechanism by which the relative amount of blood reaching various organs is controlled. (See Fig. 7-3.)

The smaller blood vessels, arterioles and capillaries, have a high inside surface area compared to large arteries, and in many capillaries blood cells must actually be squeezed to push them through. Blood flow is thereby retarded by friction and most of the arterial pressure is lost, with the result that the pressure in veins is very small. In contrast to the arteries, veins have relatively thin walls with few smooth muscle cells and less elastic connective tissue.

The dissipation of arterial pressure as blood passes through capillaries creates a practical problem—namely, how is the blood to complete the rest of its circuit back to the heart? In most cases the veins draining blood from a given organ are approximately as long as the arteries supplying it, but there is no large pressure difference to force the blood on its way. Large terrestrial mammals have a potential added problem in that the legs and lower portions of the body lie far enough below the heart that gravity further retards the return of venous blood. This problem is overcome by the widespread presence in veins of check valves that prevent back flow. (See Fig. 7-2.) The forward propulsion of blood toward the heart is largely

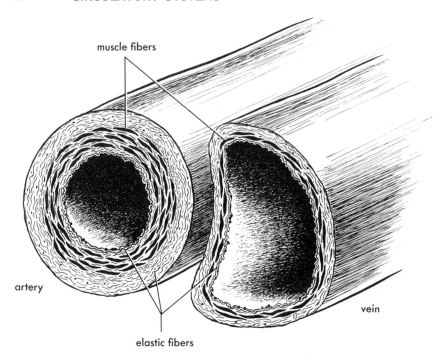

muscle fibers

artery

vein

elastic fibers

Fig. 7-3. Diagrammatic cross sections of a typical artery and vein from a vertebrate animal. Note that the artery has thicker walls containing more muscle and more elastic connective tissue.

caused by the contractions of surrounding skeletal muscles, just as in the circulatory systems of smaller and simpler animals. In mammals the expansion of the pleural cavity to fill the lungs serves also to draw venous blood into the heart, which is separated from the pleural cavity only by a thin membrane of connective tissue.

The fact that venous blood returns to the heart at a low pressure, dependent in part on muscles that are not really part of the circulatory system at all, means that filling of the heart requires special measures. In all vertebrates, and also in a few of the more active invertebrate animals such as squids, the heart consists of two chambers arranged in series; these chambers are usually called *atrium* and *ventricle*. The former receives the blood from the larger veins and is relatively thin walled. It contracts shortly before the ventricle does and fills it with blood already under a moderate pressure. The ventricle has much thicker walls and its more powerful muscle raises the pressure to the arterial level. There are check valves between atrium and ventricle and between the latter and the *aorta*, as the first main artery is called before it branches. This type of two-chambered heart has a double advantage in that the pumping is divided between two masses of muscle, and the preliminary contraction of the atrium distends the ventricle by forcing blood into it and thus stretches its muscle so that on contraction it can develop more force. This greater force results from the general property that muscles have of being elastic as well as contractile.

ORGANIZATION OF VERTEBRATE CIRCULATORY SYSTEMS

The circulatory systems of fishes include a two-chambered heart leading to a ventral aorta that divides into several lateral arteries that lead to the gills via the gill arches. (See Fig. 2-5.) After flowing through capillaries in the gills, all the blood is collected into a large dorsal aorta or into large arteries leading into the head. These in turn divide to supply arterial blood to the several organs of the body. In the digestive tract and in parts of the posterior end of the fish the blood is collected, after passing through capillaries, not into large veins leading directly to the heart but into veins that branch until they lead to still other capillaries. These are called *portal veins* in contrast to those that lead without subdivision to the heart. The portal vein from the digestive tract leads to the liver, and is hence called the *hepatic portal vein;* the others lead to the kidneys and are called *renal portal veins.* These relationships are shown diagrammatically in Fig. 7-4. The important point is that the blood passes through at least two, and sometimes three, sets of capillaries before returning to the heart. At each set there is a considerable drop in pressure, and in the portal veins the return flow of blood is assisted by valves and the squeezing of surrounding musculature.

In inquiring why the circulatory system should be organized in this way, it is important to note the advantage gained by having all blood flow first through the gills for respiratory gas exchange; thus wherever it may go next it will be well supplied with oxygen. Against this must be weighed the inefficiency caused by loss of some arterial pressure as the blood passes through the capillaries of the gills. The hepatic portal system serves to carry food molecules directly from the digestive tract to cells of the liver where many of them are stored or converted into other substances. The advantages of a renal portal system are not obvious, and it is absent in mammals.

In terrestrial vertebrates lungs replace gills as the respiratory organs, and the form of blood supply is different. In the Amphibia the lungs are supplied by large *pulmonary arteries* and drained by *pulmonary veins* that lead into a second atrium located to the left of the atrium that receives blood from the rest of the body. Both atria pump blood into the same ventricle; there oxygenated blood from the lungs is mixed to some degree with blood that comes from active organs and has been depleted

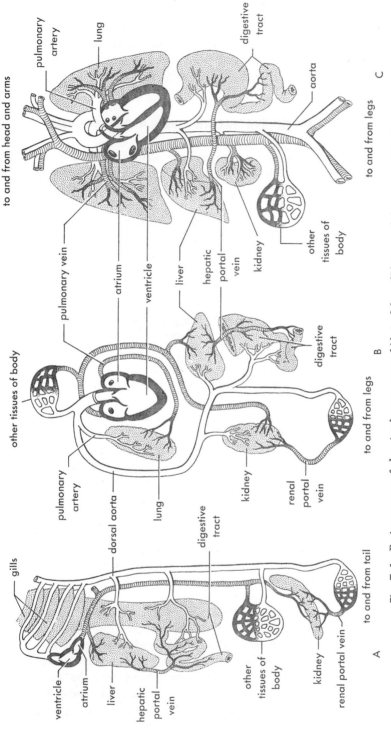

Fig. 7-4. Basic patterns of the circulatory system (A) in fishes, (B) in amphibians, and (C) in mammals. Note the locations of capillary networks where molecules can easily enter and leave the blood, and where the blood pressure drops appreciably. Veins are shaded throughout the circulatory systems, in contrast to the unshaded arteries. To test his understanding of the interrelationships of respiratory and circulatory systems the student should ask himself which vessels in all three systems carry oxygenated and unoxygenated blood.

in oxygen content. In most amphibians the skin also serves to a considerable extent as a respiratory surface, and this reduces the inefficiency of the mixing of blood in the single ventricle. In reptiles the ventricle is also subdivided to varying degrees into two chambers, one of which pumps blood into the pulmonary artery while the other supplies the rest of the body. In many reptiles the separation is adequate to channel virtually all the well-aerated blood from the pulmonary vein into the general circulation while the blood from the main veins draining the balance of the body is directed to the pulmonary arteries. In birds and mammals this separation is complete, and there are two atria and two ventricles making up a single compact mass of muscle but pumping blood through two distinct channels as diagramed in Fig. 7-4.

In all vertebrate animals there is still another part of the circulatory system, the *lymphatic vessels*. These are thin walled and begin as finely branched tubes that are almost as small as capillaries but are not connected to arteries. Small lymphatics join to form larger ones and the largest ones drain into veins. Lymphatics are provided with valves, and in some amphibians there are small *lymph hearts* that contract rather feebly to pump lymph into the veins. Otherwise, flow is entirely maintained by the squeezing action of surrounding muscles. The lymph, the fluid contained in the lymphatics, is colorless owing to the absence of the red blood cells that are so numerous in blood, but otherwise it is similar to the blood. It enters the small terminal lymphatics by diffusion from surrounding spaces between cells. Amoeboid cells, the white blood cells, sometimes force their way between the thin cells forming the walls of lymphatics, and hence are found in the lymph. Although the lymphatic system is not an open one in structure, since all its vessels are surrounded by distinct walls of cells, its function resembles that of the open blood sinuses of invertebrates in that the lymph can work its way back to the heart from all parts of the body; and this process serves to equalize the distribution of body fluids.

There are also blood sinuses in vertebrates, but they are restricted to a few specific organs. For example, the liver contains regular sinuses as well as capillaries, and the spleen is a spongy mass of tissue that serves to store blood in sinuses as well as being the location of cells that form some types of blood cell. In the placenta of pregnant mammals blood also fills sinuses, and the exchange of materials between maternal and fetal blood occurs from sinuses.

CHEMICAL SPECIALIZATIONS OF BLOOD

Blood is more than a simple salt solution populated by drifting cells; it contains several types of molecules adapted for the efficient transport of oxygen. Molecular oxygen, O_2, is not a highly reactive substance, and unlike CO_2 it can only be held in water in physical solution. When water comes into equilibrium with air, which ordinarily contains just under 21 percent oxygen, it takes into solution only about 0.5 percent of its volume of gaseous oxygen. Expressed in terms of weight, this is only a few parts per million. Hence only a small fraction of the blood pumped through the circulatory system can consist of oxygen in physical solution. Since the rate at which oxygen can be transported is often a limiting factor in the success of the animal, it is clearly very advantageous to increase the capacity of the blood to carry oxygen. This is accomplished in vertebrate animals, and also in many of the annelid worms, by *hemoglobin,* a red, iron-containing protein molecule located inside red blood cells or erythrocytes in vertebrate animals. Some mollusks and arthropods have instead a copper-containing protein called *hemocyanin* in solution in their blood.

The following typical values of the oxygen concentration attained by blood of various animals when in equilibrium with air show the effectiveness of hemoglobin and hemocyanin: mollusks and arthropods employing hemocyanin, 1 to 4 ml gaseous O_2 per 100 ml of blood; some of the burrowing marine annelids such as *Arenicola*, 9 ml per 100 ml; fishes, 10 to 16 ml per 100 ml; most birds and mammals, 15 to 20 ml per 100 ml; and marine mammals such as seals and porpoises, which use hemoglobin as a means of storing some oxygen for long dives, up to 30 ml O_2 per 100 ml blood.

Hemoglobin or other substances that serve the same function must not only take up oxygen at the respiratory surfaces, but must give it off again in the vicinity of cells that require it for their metabolism. A number of chemical compounds combine with O_2, but do it so firmly that they would be worse than useless for oxygen transport in an animal's blood because the combination would be too tight and the animal would asphyxiate even though its blood was loaded with O_2. What is needed is a molecule with flexible powers of combining loosely with oxygen at the respiratory organs and then releasing it equally freely in capillaries within range of easy diffusion to actively metabolizing cells.

To appreciate the biochemical adaptations of blood one must distinguish between the concentration of oxygen in a solution and its *partial pressure.* The former is simply the amount of oxygen per unit volume of blood, sea water, or any other solution. The partial pressure is a measure of the tendency of the oxygen to diffuse out of the solution, and it is defined as the partial pressure in a gas that is in equilibrium with the solution—that is, a volume of gas that when exposed to the solution will neither take up oxygen from it nor give off oxygen to it. The relationship of concentration to partial pressure can be made clearer by reference to Fig. 7-5, which shows diagrammatically a beaker of water and one of blood, both exposed to the same air. It does not matter for this comparison whether the blood is in a beaker or is flowing in the capillaries of some animal's respiratory surface. After both blood and water have been exposed to the air long enough to come into equilibrium with it, the partial pressure of oxygen in both solutions will be the same. The concentration, however, will be much higher in the blood because oxygen is combined with hemoglobin as well as being in physical solution. The function of hemoglobin is thus to increase the concentration of oxygen held in the blood at a given partial pressure of oxygen.

In most natural bodies of water, including the oceans, there are only enough animals or microorganisms to lower the partial pressure of oxygen slightly below that of the atmosphere, or about 21 percent of 760 mm of mercury. Hence most animals find oxygen in their environment at a partial pressure of roughly 150 mm Hg. It is at this partial pressure that their blood

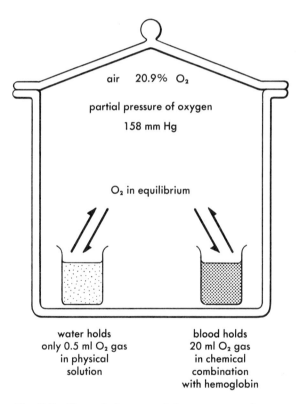

air   20.9% O_2

partial pressure of oxygen

158 mm Hg

O_2 in equilibrium

water holds
only 0.5 ml O_2 gas
in physical
solution

blood holds
20 ml O_2 gas
in chemical
combination
with hemoglobin

Fig. 7-5. Two solutions containing oxygen at the same partial pressure (because both are in equilibrium with the same gas), but with very different concentrations of oxygen. In water, oxygen is held only in solution; in blood it is held also in a loose chemical combination with the hemoglobin.

takes up oxygen, and almost exactly the same partial pressure is retained as the blood flows from respiratory surface to active tissues. The more active the metabolism of these cells, the lower will be the partial pressure of O_2 in their vicinity. A concentration gradient is thus set up; and oxygen diffuses from the blood into the cells.

Hemoglobin must now reverse the role it plays at the respiratory surfaces; the more rapidly and completely it can give off oxygen, the better will it serve the needs of the animal. In response to this need, the hemoglobin in active animals has the property of combining vigorously with O_2 only over a certain range of partial pressures; this can be illustrated quantitatively by a graph such as Fig. 7-6 in which the concentration of oxygen in the blood is plotted against the partial pressure of oxygen with which it is in equilibrium. Because the hemoglobin has the properties described by this S-shaped curve it can deliver to the active tissues a much larger amount of oxygen than would be the case if the curve were linear.

Animals that are very active and that live where the partial pressure of oxygen is always high, such as birds and oceanic squids or fast-swimming

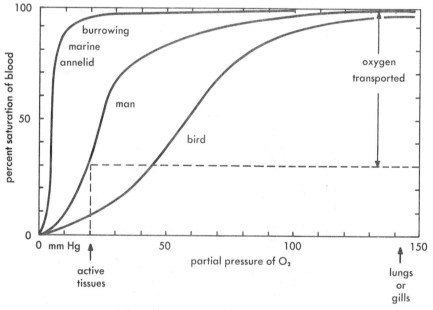

Fig. 7-6. The quantitative properties of blood in three types of animals adapted for life in environments with high and low partial pressures of oxygen. The amount of oxygen actually transported from respiratory organ to active tissue is shown for one case, but from such graphs as these one can read the amount transported under other conditions as well. In order to permit comparison of bloods having different oxygen capacities the ordinates are all percent saturation—that is, percentage of the maximum amount of oxygen held when the blood is in equilibrium with air.

fish, tend to have a kind of hemoglobin that gives off its oxygen at a fairly high partial pressure so that the active cells can obtain it rapidly along a steep concentration gradient from capillary to the mitochondria where the actual reactions with O_2 take place. Animals with hemoglobins of this type must pay the price of vulnerability to low environmental oxygen partial pressures. Should they find themselves in a situation where the oxygen has been depleted by other organisms, their blood can take up but a small fraction of its full capacity of O_2. Other kinds of animals live in environments where the oxygen is very scarce, some of the clearest examples being found among the marine annelid worms. Many of those that have especially well-developed gills also have blood containing hemoglobin or some other protein that combines in a similar loose fashion with O_2. These substances, however, have properties described by quite a different curve, such as that shown at the left of Fig. 7-6. This type of blood can take up its full capacity of oxygen at very low partial pressures, and yet give it off again at still lower partial pressures.

Hemoglobin and its role in oxygen transport is but one isolated example of the functional adaptations that render almost every part of every animal an intricate mechanism of admirable efficiency. It is impossible in an elementary account to do justice to even a few of these biological phenomena, but the reader should bear in mind that every cubic micron of protoplasm, almost every molecule, is packed with such surprises.

SUGGESTED READING LIST

FLORKIN, M. (trans. S. MORGULIS), 1949. *Biochemical evolution.* New York: Academic Press.

Fox, H. M., "Blood pigments," *Scientific American*, March 1950, p. 20.

KROGH, A., 1959. *The anatomy and physiology of capillaries.* New York: Hafner. (Revised edition edited by Landis.)

PROSSER, C. L., and BROWN, F. A., JR., 1961. *Comparative animal physiology*, 2d ed. Philadelphia: Saunders. Chapter 13.

ROMER, A. S., 1949. *The vertebrate body.* Philadelphia: Saunders. Chapter 13.

SCHOLANDER, P. F., "The wonderful net." *Scientific American,* Apr. 1957, p. 96.

WIGGERS, C. J., "The heart," *Scientific American*, May 1957, p. 74.

YOUNG, J. Z., 1957. *The life of mammals.* New York: Oxford. Chapters 13 and 14.

ZWEIFACH, B. W., "The microcirculation of the blood," *Scientific American*, Jan. 1959, p. 54.

CHAPTER EIGHT

CHEMICAL

REGULATION INTRODUCTION—In addition to the organ

systems described in previous chapters, all highly organized animals are equipped with what are usually referred to as *excretory organs*. When these are numerous, small, and widely distributed through the body they are usually called *nephridia;* in some animals they may be concentrated, as in the compact *kidneys* of mollusks, arthropods, and vertebrates. The term "excretory" is applied because all of the organs produce a fluid urine in which the animal disposes of some by-products of its metabolism, such as ammonia, NH_3, or urea $(NH_2)_2C=O$. But excretion of metabolic by-products is only one aspect of a much more fundamental *regulatory* function of these organs. Urine is a solution generally similar to blood, lymph, or the tissue fluids that always bathe or flow close to the cells of excretory organs, but the composition of urine is adjusted to differ from that of blood or tissue fluids in a manner that corresponds to the chemical needs of the animal. Substances that are too abundant are more concentrated in urine than in blood, and vice versa. Furthermore, these differences between blood and urine are not fixed but are varied from time to time according to changing chemical conditions inside the animal or in its surroundings. It is thus more appropriate to refer to these as organ systems for *regulatory excretion*.

Living organisms first arose in the ocean, in all probability, and the internal fluids of all the simpler marine animals now extant are very similar to sea water in the proportions of the major ions of salt water, Na^+, K^+, Ca^{2+}, Mg^{2+}, Cl^-, and SO_4^{2-}. Potassium tends to be more abundant and magnesium less so in their blood than in salt water. But many animals of all levels of complexity are able to live in fresh-water streams and lakes and on land; in order to do so, their enzymes and other protoplasmic mechanisms also require an ionic environment that must remain within close limits, even though different from the composition of sea water. This freedom to depart from the ancestral sea water requires that an animal regulate the composition of its fluids as a simple marine animal need not do. The matter was put succinctly by the nineteenth-century physiologist Claude Bernard in a much-quoted epigram: *La fixité du milieu intérieur est la condition de la vie libre* (Constancy of the internal medium is essential for a free life).

This sort of internal regulation of the animal body is of tremendous importance and is designated *homeostasis*, meaning the maintenance of a constant or nearly constant state. It is one of the unique attributes of living cells and organs that they achieve homeostasis so well and with such compact mechanisms. Many essential types of homeostatic regulation are performed by individual cells that respond to variations in their environment by taking corrective action to offset departures from the most favorable state of the variable in question. The kidneys of animals perform simultaneously several independent types of homeostatic regulation by selective action on individual substances present in the blood.

OSMOTIC REGULATION IN FRESH WATER

Consider the basic problem of any marine animal, protozoan or fish, that suddenly finds itself in fresh water where the concentration of ions is much lower outside its body than in its tissue fluids. Parts of its surface are permeable to small molecules and ions (as a very minimum it must have a respiratory surface), and hence both the ions and water itself tend to move along the concentration gradients that are necessarily present across these permeable surfaces. Salts will be lost and water will diffuse inward, but the latter process is usually much the more rapid of the two, because water penetrates most living membranes quite easily and because in addition to small ions the internal fluids contain many larger molecules that cannot diffuse outward at all or only at negligible rates. Hence the inward diffusion of water is not matched by outward diffusion of other molecules, and the internal fluids tend to become progressively more dilute. This process is often called *osmosis,* and if unchecked it produces a swelling and the eventual death of the animal.

Fortunately, all fresh-water animals effect osmotic homeostasis by carrying out some kind of regulatory excretion that "bails out" the excess of water that is always tending to diffuse inward. This requires the excretion of urine that is more dilute than the blood or internal fluids, and the separation of such a dilute solution from the internal fluids requires active chemical work on the part of specialized protoplasm somewhere in the animal's body. So important is this regulatory excretion that it often requires elaborate organs and even consumes under some circumstances an appreciable fraction of the total metabolic energy of the animal.

THE STRUCTURE OF EXCRETORY ORGANS

Even Protozoa have an organelle for regulatory excretion, called the *contractile vacuole*. This is a fluid-filled vesicle in the cytoplasm that grows slowly from time to time and then empties to the outside. It contains a more dilute solution than the cytoplasm, and contractile vacuoles are formed and emptied much more frequently in fresh-water protozoans than in their close relatives that live in sea water. Some Protozoa can live in a wide range of salinities; the more dilute is the water in which they are studied, the more active are their contractile vacuoles. The exact mechanism for filling the contractile vacuole is not known, but its wall is a membrane only about 60 Ångstrom units thick (an Ångstrom unit, abbreviated Å, is 10^{-8} cm). The cytoplasm close to this membrane contains a layer of mitochondria and a dense layer of vacuoles 200 to 2000 Å in diameter that probably open into the vacuole to fill it. Since mitochondria are known to contain many of the enzymes concerned with the stepwise breakdown of food molecules to yield energy, it is reasonable to assume that they are providing the energy for the chemical work of separating from the cytoplasm the dilute "urine" to fill the contractile vacuole.

Although the contractile vacuole is an important intracellular organelle for regulatory excretion of water, much of the regulation of many cells occurs through the general cell surface, without any structural specialization that has yet been recognized. Some fresh-water protozoans have no contractile vacuoles, nor are they found in fresh-water coelenterates, which nevertheless maintain their protoplasm at a higher salt concentration than the surrounding water. Yet flatworms, most of the roundworms, and all annelid worms have some sort of specialized excretory organs that consist of tubules emptying through pores on the surface of the body. These often branch, and their inner ends are thin walled and located close to blood or tissue fluids such as those in the body cavity. In the flatworms the inner end of each tubule consists of a single specialized cell with a tuft of cilia that beat continuously and set up a gentle current along the tubule toward the outside. (See Fig. 8-1.) These cells are called *flame cells* because their cilia appear under the microscope to flicker like a candle. In annelid worms the excretory tubules begin with a funnel-shaped opening from one segment of the body cavity, and after a long series of convolutions the tubule drains into an external pore opening to the outside of the animal's body.

In mollusks and arthropods there are similar excretory tubules but they are usually longer and are concentrated into definite kidneys that empty to the outside through larger collecting tubules. In some crustaceans urine is collected in a thin-walled bladder before being discharged to the outside by two pores located on the head. Although the inner ends of the tubules usually do not make a direct connection to the body cavity, they are closely

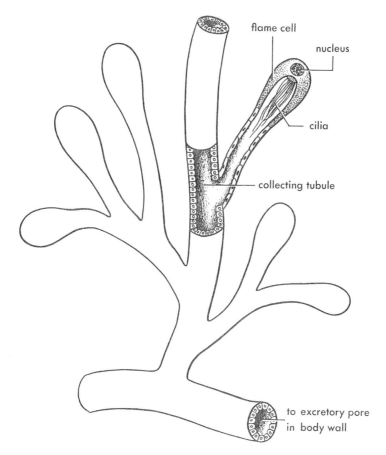

Fig. 8-1. A portion of the excretory system of a flatworm. Note that each tubule begins with a flame cell, and that the tuft of cilia forming the "flame" sets up a current in the fluid within each tubule.

surrounded by the blood of the open circulatory system. Insects differ from the Crustacea in having as excretory organs a series of long, thin *Malpighian tubules* ramifying through the body and emptying into the posterior end of the intestine. Diagrams of these two types of excretory systems found in arthropods are shown in Fig. 8-2.

Vertebrate animals have paired kidneys each consisting of thousands of kidney tubules or *nephrons* that are several millimeters long and are interwined together to form the paired kidneys shown in Fig. 2-5. All begin with a tubule that is in close contact with a network of capillaries and all converge into a single duct, the *ureter*, that leads to the urinary bladder. This in turn is connected to the outside by a single duct, the *urethra*. The important difference between the vertebrate nephron and the excretory

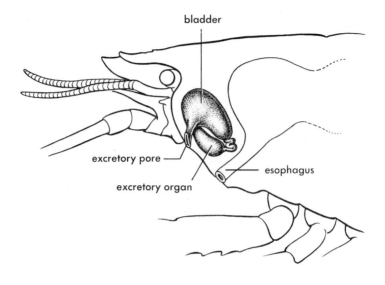

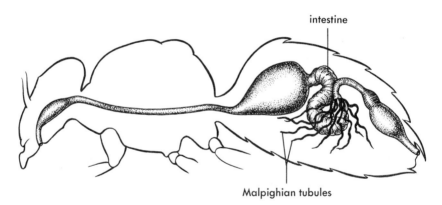

Fig. 8-2. The excretory system of a crustacean (above) and an insect (below). Note that in the former a dilute fluid urine is excreted directly to the water outside the animal. In insects the Malpighian tubules empty into the digestive tract, and in many cases uric acid is the chief compound in which excess nitrogen is excreted in semisolid form.

tubules of other phyla is the intimate association of the inner end of the nephron with the circulatory system. This association takes two forms, the *glomerulus* at the very beginning of the nephron, and the capillaries that cluster around the tubule along much of its length until it joins other nephrons to empty into the collecting tubules.

The glomerulus is a tuft of capillaries supplied by an arteriole that arises as one of many branches of the renal artery carrying blood to each kidney. The walls of these capillaries are very thin, and the electron microscope reveals that they are penetrated by many pores too small to be resolved by the light microscope. Unlike most capillaries, those of a glomerulus drain into another small artery, with rather muscular walls, instead of into a small vein. This in turn leads to a second set of capillaries that pass close to the walls of one or more nephrons, and only after passing through these capillaries does the blood flow into veins for a return trip to the heart. The glomerulus is located inside a *Bowman's capsule,* formed by an enlargement at the beginning of the nephron. There is thus an arrangement whereby fluids can leave the blood stream through the walls of the glomerular capillaries and move directly into the inner end of a tubule leading to the urinary bladder. Along much of the length of the kidney tubule there is further opportunity for exchange between capillaries and fluid inside the tubule, but here it must occur across not only capillary walls but the cells forming the tubule. These structural arrangements are shown diagrammatically in Fig. 8-3.

Glomeruli are especially large and well developed in fresh-water fish, whereas in marine fish they are smaller and less numerous. A few species of marine fish lack them altogether, and have nephrons that receive only capillaries around the tubular portion. A question of marked interest is why there should be this correlation between the kind of water in which the fish live and the microscopic anatomy of their kidneys.

THE FORMATION OF URINE

In all excretory tubules, from those of flatworms beginning with a flame cell to those of mammals arising as a Bowman's capsule, the contents of the inner end of the tubule is a solution that is more like blood or body fluids than is the urine. All these tubules are potentially leaks in the animal's circulatory system or holes through which its body fluids would tend to escape, but the solution inside the tubule is being "processed" as it moves along. Some substances are being added and others removed, and the end result is the excretion of a solution differing from the internal fluids in a manner that achieves a homeostasis of the internal environment. As far as is known, the same basic processes are at work in all types of excretory tubule; but these are more efficient, and better understood, in the case of vertebrate animals. Consequently this elementary account of the mechanisms of urine formation will be confined to the vertebrate nephron.

The first step obviously occurs at the glomerulus, and analysis of fluid withdrawn from Bowman's capsule by micropipettes has shown that the only important difference between this fluid and the blood plasma is the

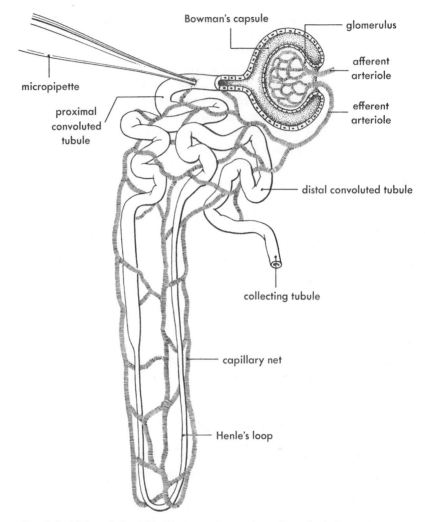

Fig. 8-3. Enlarged diagrammatic view of a nephron from the kidney of a vertebrate animal. A micropipette is being used to withdraw a minute amount of fluid from the tubule for chemical analysis. Such experiments show that all but the largest molecules in the blood diffuse rapidly (that is, are filtered) through the thin walls of the glomerular capillaries.

absence of blood cells and protein molecules. In fact, the fluid is just what one would expect on the assumption that all but very large molecules can escape by filtration through the pores in the walls of glomerular capillaries that are visible under the electron microscope. Furthermore, measurements of the rate at which such a filtrate of plasma is exuded into the whole set of nephrons in a human kidney reveal the startling fact that more than

100 ml are thus lost from the circulatory system every minute. Obviously some compensating process must intervene, since the normal output of urine is only about 1 ml per minute. This process is the *reabsorption* of water and other molecules from the tubules back into the capillaries that surround them.

Along with over 99 percent of the water in the glomerular filtrate other molecules are reabsorbed in a selective fashion. Glucose and amino acids are almost totally withdrawn and cannot normally be detected in the urine at all, although the microanalysis of fluid in the tubule close to Bowman's capsule discloses their presence there (see Fig. 8-3). On the other hand, only about half the urea is reabsorbed, so that the net result of filtration and reabsorption is that its concentration is much higher in urine than in blood. Some substances are also moved directly from the capillaries around the nephron into the fluid inside it; this has been demonstrated by injecting dyes such as phenol red into the renal portal veins of amphibians after blocking the renal arteries. This special type of blood supply to their kidneys brings such blood only to the tubules and not to the glomeruli, but the dye was nevertheless recovered from the urine. In short, various molecules are moved at widely different rates out of the nephron and back into the blood, and in a few cases the reverse process also occurs.

It is surprising at first thought that our kidneys and those of most other vertebrates should operate in the manner just described. Why should such a large potential leak from the blood stream be tolerated? The answer is believed to lie in large part in our evolutionary history, as the remote descendants of fishes. Bearing in mind the basic osmotic problem of fresh-water animals—removal of the water that diffuses in from outside—we can readily imagine that kidneys equipped with glomeruli would be effective in removing such excess water. Having separated a considerable volume of blood plasma by filtration across the very thin capillaries of the glomerulus, the rest of the nephron has the function of selectively reabsorbing much of this water and the various dissolved molecules. The total salt concentration of the blood and tissue fluids of fresh-water fishes is somewhat less than half that of sea water, though of course it is still well above the concentration of salts in fresh water.

These considerations also help to explain why marine fish should have small glomeruli or none at all, for their body fluids have nearly the same total salt concentration as fresh-water fish, and indeed all vertebrates are similar in this respect. The muscles in the walls of the small arteries supplying and draining the glomeruli also control the amount of blood flowing through them, and this is especially important in fishes that move back and forth between fresh and salt water. In other words, the vertebrate kidney seems designed for the needs of fresh-water fish, and this observation together with other evidence leads biologists to believe that the earliest fishes lived in fresh water and that present-day marine fish as well as terrestrial verte-brates are descended from them.

Quite apart from these historical reasons for our kidneys being what they are, the system of filtration and selective reabsorption has certain ad-vantages from the point of view of regulation, which is the most basically important aspect of kidney function. Let us consider the regulation by the kidney of the blood levels of a few typical substances, beginning with water itself. Since over 99 percent of the water in the glomerular filtrate is ordi-narily reabsorbed, a very small change in this reabsorption will produce a large change in the total rate of water loss; for example, a shift from 99 percent to 98 percent reabsorption means a doubling of the water output. Thus the needs of the animal for water elimination or water conservation can be met by slight alterations in the rate of reabsorption. Another im-portant example is the regulation of the potassium ion, the concentration of which must be kept within certain approximate limits in the blood, since it is required for the normal functioning of all cells. Because foods vary widely in their potassium content, the blood level tends to fluctuate with diet. In the nephron a large part of the K^+ is reabsorbed along with the water, but the exact amount varies according to the concentration of K^+ in the blood; if this is higher than normal, less is reabsorbed and more is lost in the urine. Similarly, other ions are reabsorbed at different rates to achieve a homeo-static regulation of their level in the blood stream.

Substances that must be retained, such as glucose and amino acids, are totally reabsorbed, and their absence in the urine means that along part of the length of the nephron their concentration in the fluid inside the tubule is zero or too low to measure. Yet just outside these portions of the nephron are capillaries with blood containing these same substances in appreciable concentrations. Hence almost all of the glucose, for example, is moved out of the nephron against a concentration gradient. In this and several other cases substances are moved across the walls of the cells that form the nephron by active transport, a process that was discussed in Chap-ter 4 as it occurs during absorption from the intestine.

NITROGEN EXCRETION

Most animals take in with their food more amino acids and other compounds containing nitrogen than they require either as food or in the synthesis of new proteins for repair or growth. As a result, there is an excess of nitrogen that is eliminated by excreting different nitrogenous compounds. A very common by-product of amino acid metabolism in the cells of all animals is ammonia, which in aqueous solution takes the form of the ammonium ion, NH_4^+. This is both readily soluble and also rather toxic, so that it cannot be allowed to exceed a very low concentration. The ammonium ion is the chief vehicle for the excretion of excess nitrogen in most invertebrate animals except the insects and some of the terrestrial snails. It is also used by fishes, aquatic stages of amphibians, crocodiles, and aquatic turtles, all of which have an abundant supply of water and excrete a copious, dilute urine.

Terrestrial vertebrates and marine fishes have problems of water conservation, and it is apparently difficult for them to spare enough water to dilute the ammonium ions arising from excess nitrogen intake. Instead, their nitrogen excretion is achieved in the form of urea or other nitrogenous substances that are much less toxic than ammonium ions. In addition to urea, many marine fish excrete considerable quantities of trimethylamine oxide, $(CH_3)_3N{=}O$, which gives rise to one of the characteristic odors of dead fish. The most interesting adaptation of nitrogen excretion to terrestrial life and its attendant problems of water conservation is the conversion of excess nitrogenous products into the nearly insoluble substance uric acid, a larger molecule containing four NH groups. This is the material that forms the semisolid whitish paste excreted by birds, snakes, and lizards. Terrestrial snails also excrete mostly uric acid, and many insects excrete it via their Malpighian tubules; in other insects it is deposited in various parts of the body—for example, as the white scales on the outer surfaces of the wings in certain white butterflies.

These adaptations to fit the nitrogenous excretory product to the animal's way of life are achieved to a large extent by cells of the liver and kidney, which convert excess amino acids and other nitrogen-containing compounds into various proportions of ammonium ion, urea, trimethylamine oxide, or uric acid, all of which can be excreted by their kidneys. Not only do all these cells achieve an immediate type of homeostasis, they may change the entire direction of their biochemical work according to the needs of the animal. This is most clearly exemplified in the embryos of snakes, lizards, and birds, which must develop from one cell to a complete animal without any water except that present in the original egg. During the first few days of their development ammonium ion is produced, and some of it escapes through the shell as gaseous NH_3. Later, as their organ systems become more fully formed and effectively functional, urea and uric acid predominate in turn. Since no liquids or solids can be extruded to the outside, uric acid simply accumulates just inside the shell.

There are many other known cases where kidneys or other organs adjust their activities in such a way as to achieve homeostasis, and still more phenomena of this type await adequate investigation. The above examples suffice to demonstrate the complex web of interactions that are required to maintain the harmoniously organized internal environment of a living animal.

SUGGESTED READING LIST

EDNEY, E. B., 1957. *The water relations of terrestrial arthropods.* Cambridge, Eng.: Cambridge University Press.

PROSSER, C. L., and BROWN, F. A., JR., 1961. *Comparative animal physiology,* 2d ed. Philadelphia: Saunders. Chapters 2, 3, and 6.

SCHMIDT-NIELSEN, K. AND B., "The desert rat," *Scientific American,* July 1953, p. 73.

SMITH, H. W., 1953. *From fish to philosopher.* Boston: Little, Brown.

———, 1956. *Principles of renal physiology.* New York: Oxford University Press.

———, "The kidney," *Scientific American,* Dec. 1953, p. 40.

YAPP, W. B., 1960. *An introduction to animal physiology,* 2d ed. New York: Oxford University Press. Chapter 2.

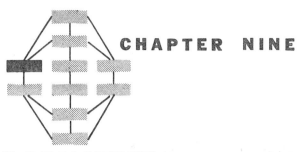

CHAPTER NINE

REPRODUCTIVE

SYSTEMS

INTRODUCTION—The living animals are here today because their ancestors succeeded in reproducing themselves more effectively than other competing forms of life. By far the most common way in which new individuals of the same species are produced is sexual reproduction, in which two cells called *gametes* fuse to form a one-celled *zygote* that in turn divides repeatedly to grow into the new individual. The basic phenomena that underlie this vital process of reproduction are treated in other books of this series, *Genetics, Cell Structure and Function,* and *Evolution;* hence this chapter will be confined to the organ systems of animals that produce the gametes, facilitate their coming together, and serve to protect and nourish the resulting progeny.

The organs where gametes are produced are called *gonads,* and in almost all metazoan animals there are two specialized kinds of gametes. A larger type called the *ovum* (pl. *ova*) contains stored food materials (mostly fat, some proteins, and a complete collection of vitamins) that will nourish the developing zygote. The smaller and far more numerous type, called *spermatozoa,* or *sperm* for short, swim actively by means of flagellae, and contain very little stored food. Usually the two types are produced in different types of gonads, and most commonly an adult animal is either a male with *testes* that produce sperm, or a female whose reproductive organs are called *ovaries* because they produce ova. There are exceptions to this rule, and in many invertebrates, especially in the phylum Platyhelminthes, ovaries and testes occur in the same animal, which is called a *hermaphrodite* (see Fig. 2-2).

There are also several types of *asexual reproduction.* One that occurs in some coelenterates and flatworms is the breaking apart of an adult into two or more pieces, each of which then grows and re-forms the parts it lacks to reconstitute a complete animal. Sometimes the fragments are roughly equal in size; more often, one is smaller and removes no vital organs from the "parent" animal. This process is so similar to regeneration after loss or damage of parts of the body that it is considered at length in *Develop-*

ment in this series. In other cases the ovum does not fuse with a sperm, but, starting in the female reproductive tract, it develops by successive stages into a normal adult. This process, called *parthenogenesis,* is fairly widespread among invertebrates and can be brought about artificially even in mammals. In most animals where it occurs at all, however, it is replaced by sexual reproduction from time to time, for reasons of long-term strategy of survival discussed in *Evolution* and *Genetics.*

GONADS AND GENITAL DUCTS

Ovaries and testes are usually rather compact organs containing not only cells that divide to form the gametes but others that serve as supporting connective tissue. In some animals certain of these so-called *interstitial cells* of the gonads produce hormones that coordinate the activities of the gonads with other parts of the body.

In coelenterates the gonads are compact masses of cells that give off gametes directly into the surrounding water. In many flatworms ovarian or testicular tissue is divided into numerous small pockets widely scattered through the body of the animal (see Fig. 2-2). Since they lie relatively deep inside the animal, they can only discharge the gametes (suspended in a solution similar to tissue fluids) through a series of branching ducts leading through a genital pore to the outside. Nematode worms usually have paired ovaries or testes—or both, since many are hermaphroditic. In annelids the gonads are paired organs in each of several segments in the central portion of the body, and gametes are often discharged via the body cavity and through openings from it to the outside. Mollusks and arthropods have paired gonads with well-developed genital ducts leading to the outside. Examples of complex reproductive systems in the male and female bee are shown diagrammatically in Fig. 9-1.

In vertebrate animals the paired gonads are inside the body cavity or close to the lining. In some but not all mammals the testes are contained in a pouch (see Fig. 9-2), the *scrotum,* which extends outside the body wall, but this pouch is formed by an outpocketing of the abdominal cavity. The ducts that convey sperm of vertebrate animals to the outside are often shared in part with the excretory system, as in mammals; in most invertebrate animals the excretory ducts are quite separate from the genital openings. In many but not all of the fishes, and in most amphibians, reptiles and birds, the urinary and genital ducts and the anus open into a common chamber called the *cloaca,* which has a single cloacal aperture through which feces, urine, or gametes may be released, according to circumstances. (See Fig. 4-1.)

The portion of the female reproductive tract that conveys ova from the ovary to other chambers or to the outside is called an *oviduct.* Often the

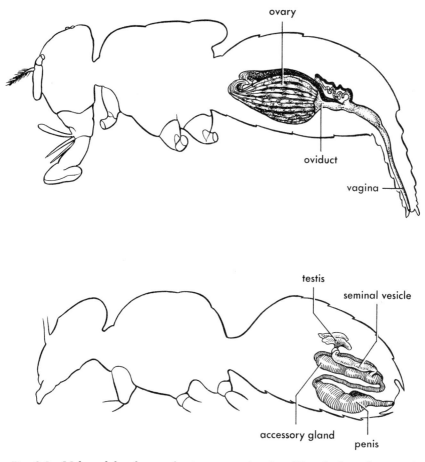

Fig. 9-1. Male and female reproductive systems in a bee. Note the large fraction of the abdomen that is filled by ovaries and accessory glands.

oviduct is lined with glands that secrete a protective shell around the ovum. In animals where the young develop inside the female the portion of the reproductive tract where this occurs is usually called a *uterus*.

EXTERNAL AND INTERNAL FERTILIZATION

In most aquatic invertebrate animals the ova and sperm are released into the water, the sperm swimming to ova probably under the attraction of special chemical substances released by the latter. Even in these animals, however, the union of gametes is not entirely a matter of chance, for the ova and sperm are released at approximately the same time

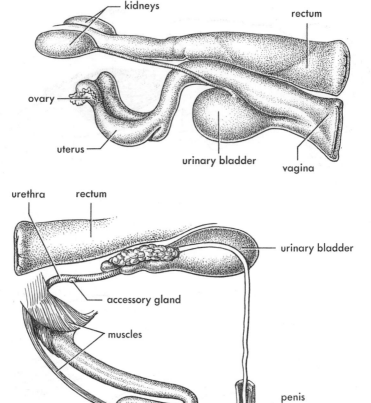

Fig. 9-2. Reproductive systems of female (above) and male (below) mammals (cow and bull).

and place as a result of courtship behavior carried out by the two adults. Nevertheless, the process of external fertilization is a relatively wasteful one, and large numbers of gametes must be produced in order that a few zygotes may succeed in growing into mature animals. Any arrangement that increases the likelihood of sperm fertilizing ova and of zygotes growing into mature animals is clearly advantageous to the species, since it permits a new generation to reach maturity with a smaller investment in gamete production.

One of many devices evolved by various animals to meet this need is internal fertilization. In this system the ova are retained inside some portion of the female reproductive tract until they complete part of their development; the sperm must, of course, reach the ovum before this development begins. Another general method for increasing the chances that a zygote will survive and grow to maturity is to have it surrounded by a protective case or shell; here, again, it is necessary for the sperm to reach the ovum before the shell is laid down around it.

A wide variety of methods are employed to deliver sperm into the female reproductive tract. In some arthropods the sperm are enclosed inside a capsule that is inserted into the female genital tract either by the male or the female using one of the jointed appendages. More commonly the male is equipped with a *penis,* a tubular structure that is inserted into the female genital opening, which in animals employing this type of internal fertilization is called a *vagina.* In addition to glands in the female reproductive tract that secrete shells or protective membranes around the eggs, both male and female genital ducts receive from other glands watery fluids in which ova or sperm are suspended.

Internal fertilization is not confined to the most highly organized phyla; its occurrence is related to the need to provide a protected environment for the developing young. The tapeworms (phylum Platyhelminthes), for example, are intestinal parasites that reproduce by discharging eggs to the outside via the feces of the host animal, and in their complex system of internal fertilization the males deliver sperm into a vagina by means of a penis. In this case it is the need for very tough impenetrable shells around the eggs that makes internal fertilization necessary. Aquatic animals are more likely to employ external fertilization than terrestrial ones because an unprotected zygote can often survive and grow in the water, even that of a highly organized animal such as a fish, a crustacean, or a squid.

THE PROTECTION AND NOURISHMENT OF DEVELOPING YOUNG

The means of protection and nourishment vary widely among animal groups. For example, a zygote fertilized externally usually secretes around itself some sort of a membrane, often of jellylike consistency such as that surrounding a frog's egg; but no single-celled ovum or zygote can produce as heavy a shell as is laid down around the embryo of many terrestrial animals by glands lining the uterus. Land snails and insects produce small eggs with very tough shells that are almost impermeable to water, and many insects lay their eggs in locations favorable to development. Some species of insects lay their eggs in burrows into which they also carry food that is later eaten by the developing young insects.

Zygotes of animals that lay eggs with resistant shells must develop inside these shells until they are large enough and fully enough formed to break out and fend for themselves. Their food supply during this period is the yolk contained in the cytoplasm of the ovum, or other substances laid down in the female reproductive tract just prior to the secretion of the shell. The most familiar and the most highly specialized example of this type of egg occurs in birds. In the familiar hen's egg the actual embryo forms only a small speck on the enormous zygote consisting mostly of yolk. The white of a bird's egg is added by the walls of the oviduct just before formation of the hard outer shell, and it serves both as protection and later as a source of protein food. The eggs of many fishes, reptiles, and virtually all birds are protected by the parents after being laid in specially constructed nests. In birds the brooding by the parents keeps the eggs from cooling or overheating, and in a few kinds of birds and in certain fish it is the male rather than the female that cares for the eggs.

A greater degree of protection of the young and a more continuous provision of food are achieved in most mammals by means of the *placenta,* a special elaboration of the uterus by which materials are exchanged between the blood of the mother and that of the developing embryo. Placental nourishment of the young also occurs in many of the sharks and related fishes, and even in a few invertebrate animals—for example, certain of the scorpions. It is far more highly developed and efficient in the placental mammals (which include all mammals except the egg-laying monotremes and the marsupials whose young are born at a very immature stage and develop further in the protection of the mother's pouch, from which they can also reach her mammary glands). The embryos of placental mammals are entirely dependent upon the placenta, receiving through it both food molecules and oxygen and giving off excretory products to the mother's blood. Even the hemoglobin of mammalian embryos is adjusted to this stage of life by having an oxygen dissociation curve differing from that of maternal blood in such a way as to facilitate transfer of oxygen from mother to embryo across the membrane that separates the two blood streams.

A great variety of special organs play important roles in the reproduction of various animals. The abdominal appendages of many female crustaceans, for example, have provisions for attachment of the eggs, so that early stages of development can occur in this partly protected location. Certain fish have gill-like structures that are used not to gain oxygen from the water but rather to give it off to developing eggs that are laid in water having a low partial pressure of oxygen. The males of a few specialized frogs have individual pockets in the skin of the back into which they place the eggs after fertilization and where the young develop for a considerable time. In pigeons a special crop gland gives off so-called pigeon milk in both males and females, which is fed to the young after hatching, much as young mammals are fed by milk secreted from mammary glands.

These examples could multiplied, but those already given demonstrate that many special structures have come into existence to serve the needs of reproduction along with care and nourishment of the developing young. The fact that these special organs are needed only intermittently, however, raises an important problem. A gill, a stomach, or a heart must function almost continuously, but reproduction in most animals occurs only at certain stages in life and is often confined to certain seasons of the year. Thus the reproductive organs of most animals undergo cycles of functioning, and when not needed they are often reduced in size. These cycles are particularly marked in the female, and perhaps most of all in female mammals, where the uterus goes through great changes in preparation for the formation of a placenta. Animals therefore need not only the reproductive organs themselves, but the means to regulate their variation in functional capacity.

SUGGESTED READING LIST

MAXIMOW, A. A., and BLOOM, W. A., 1957. *A textbook of histology*, 7th ed. Philadelphia: Saunders. Chapters 29-31.

PINCUS, G., "Fertilization in mammals," *Scientific American*, March 1951, p. 44.

ROMER, A. S., 1949. *The vertebrate body*. Philadelphia: Saunders. Chapter 12.

RUCH, T. C., and FULTON, J. G., 1960. *A textbook of physiology*, 18th ed. Philadelphia: Saunders. Chapters 57 and 58.

TURNER, C. D., 1960. *General endocrinology*, 3d ed. Philadelphia: Saunders. Chapters 8-11.

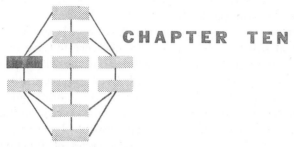

CHAPTER TEN

COORDINATION

OF

FUNCTION

INTRODUCTION—If an animal's muscles contracted and relaxed in a random fashion, while the arterioles shunted blood here and there and the heart beat faster or more slowly without regard to other events in an animal's body, convulsions and death would soon result. Such anarchy is replaced by harmony of action, thanks to special organ systems having the primary function of controlling bodily functions. Best known of these is the nervous system, but this is aided by, and intimately interrelated with, a system of endocrine glands that release hormones into the blood stream to regulate the growth or activities of other tissues.

THE STRUCTURE OF NERVOUS SYSTEMS

All multicellular animals contain elongated nerve cells, called *neurons,* collected together into parallel bundles called *nerve trunks.* Any nerve trunk large enough to be visible with the unaided eye contains hundreds or sometimes thousands of neurons. It is clear that these control the contractions of muscles and the conduction of information from sense organs to the rest of the animal, because when the nerve trunks are cut, the muscles remain relaxed and the animal ceases to react to stimulation of the corresponding sense organs. Even in some of the ciliates there are intracellular fibrils that run just below the cell membrane and connect the basal bodies of cilia or groups of cilia. When they are cut, the beating of the several cilia loses its coordinated timing and is much less effective in moving the animal through the water. Coelenterates achieve coordination of their bodily movements by a network of neurons, a so-called *nerve net,* which, however, consists of distinct cells. It ramifies throughout the body, although the neurons are more concentrated around the mouth of some coelenterates than elsewhere.

Neurons have a cell body containing a nucleus and cytoplasm much like that of other cells, and from this radiate out one or more highly elongated processes. One type, called an *axon*, usually extends for some distance, and it is axons that make up the bulk of the visible nerve trunks. The axons run parallel to one another, and each is surrounded along its length by a series of *sheath cells* (often called Schwann cells). During embryonic development the axon fits into an indentation in the sheath cell and then rotates around its axis during subsequent growth of the two cells, carrying with it the adjacent sheath cell membrane so that the axon comes to lie in a sort of "jelly-roll" of many layers of cell membrane. This compound membrane, called the *myelin* sheath, contains alternate layers of fat and protein molecules, and when sufficiently thick it gives the group of axons a whitish appearance. (See Fig. 10-1.)

Even within any one nerve trunk the axons vary greatly in the size and thickness of the sheath formed from sheath-cell membranes; the smallest are almost invisible in the light microscope, having diameters of less than 0.2 micron and only a single layer of sheath-cell membrane. The largest, found in some of the cephalopods and annelids, are a few hundred microns thick. In vertebrate animals the larger axons have thicker myelin sheaths, and the axon proper may be as much as 50 microns in diameter. Some axons are extraordinarily long; those running from the spinal cord to the extremities of large mammals may reach a length of several feet. While axons ordinarily remain about the same diameter along most of their length, they often branch near their ends, and the individual branches are usually smaller than the axon that gave rise to them.

In addition to axons the cell bodies of many neurons give off smaller processes, which are called *dendrites* because they are usually highly branched like trees. Cell bodies and dendrites are usually aggregated into concentrated masses of nervous tissue, called *ganglia* (sing. *ganglion*), and an animal's main assemblage of ganglia is called its *central nervous system*. Within ganglia the ends of axons come into very close proximity with cell bodies and dendrites of other neurons, and these places of contact, called *synapses*, are of the greatest importance in the functioning of nervous systems. At a synapse the two cell membranes are usually somewhat thickened, and the gap between the two may be as small as 200 Å and hence only visible by means of the electron microscope. Synapses also occur between cells of the coelenterate nerve net, and a specialized type of synapse occurs where the axon of a motor nerve ends on a muscle cell. Within the central nervous systems of vertebrate animals one finds bundles of axons with myelin sheaths much like nerve trunks found elsewhere in the body. These are often sufficiently concentrated to give a whitish appearance to the tissue. Such parts of central nervous systems are called "white matter" to distinguish them from "gray matter," which contains predominantly cell bodies and dendrites. Ganglia also contain large numbers of cells called *glia* that

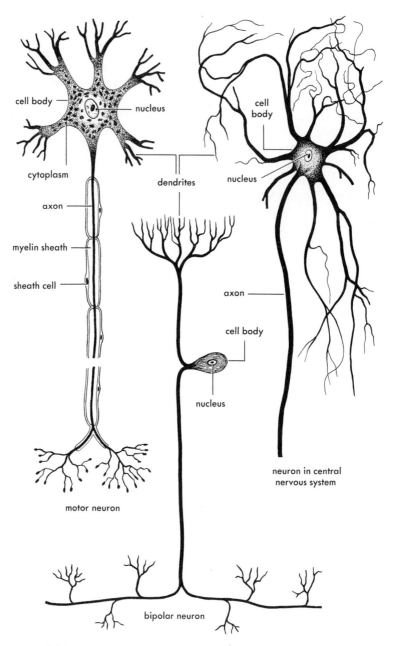

Fig. 10-1. Three neurons of common types. The one at the left shows the myelin sheath formed from sheath cell membranes rolled several layers thick around the axon proper. Many neurons are much longer, relative to the diameter of axon and cell body, and many have much thinner myelin sheaths or only a single cell membrane surrounding the axon. Within nerve trunks outside of the central nervous system even the nonmyelinated axons lie inside sheath cells.

bear a superficial resemblance to connective tissue cells. Their relationship to neurons is so close, however, that they may well be the counterparts, in the central nervous system, of the sheath cells that lay down myelin around the axons of peripheral neurons. It has been suggested recently that glial cells may participate actively in the long-term regulation of an animal's behavior by the central nervous system.

In all flatworms and roundworms the nervous system consists of two main nerve trunks with numerous cross connections, and with a slightly larger ganglion in the head region. This tendency to concentrate central nervous system tissue into the anterior end is more pronounced in annelids and arthropods, which also have a double nerve cord running the length of the animal with cross-connecting nerve trunks in each segment. This double nerve cord is located ventral to the digestive tract, and the main, anterior part of the central nervous system, which in these animals is prominent enough to call a brain, consists of ganglia lying both ventral and dorsal to the digestive tube with lateral connectives forming a ring around the esophagus. (See Fig. 10-2.) The concentration of ganglia into the anterior end is related to the corresponding tendency toward concentration there of the major sense organs. These include eyes and sensory cells close to the mouth that are stimulated mechanically and chemically by food and other substances. In mollusks the central nervous system has no simple structural pattern, but there are sizable ganglia near all the major organs such as the digestive tract and the foot. In the cephalopods there is a brain near the well-developed eyes and mouth, and like that of the annelids and arthropods it takes the form of a ring surrounding the esophagus.

In vertebrate animals the central nervous system is constructed on quite a different plan, consisting of a single nerve cord that is dorsal to the digestive tract and hollow along its whole length. The anterior part of the central nervous system is the brain, which is continuous with the spinal cord in the thorax, abdomen, and tail. The axial skeleton, the chain of vertebrae and the skull, surround and protect the spinal cord and brain respectively. The spinal canal lying deep inside the spinal cord connects with the larger *ventricles* of the brain; both are filled with cerebrospinal fluid that is similar to lymph. The body of a vertebrate animal is segmented, though less obviously so than in annelids and arthropods, and this is reflected in the emergence from the spinal cord of two *spinal nerves* through notches in the sides of each vertebra. In addition to the brain and spinal cord there is in vertebrate animals a chain of paired *sympathetic ganglia* lying lateral and ventral to the spinal cord in the thorax and abdomen, and connected to the spinal nerves by connecting nerve trunks. (See Fig. 10-3.)

From the brain arise paired *cranial nerves*, and these differ greatly in size and importance. The most anterior pair, or first cranial nerves, are *olfactory;* the second pair are the *optic nerves* connecting the brain with the eye. The eighth are the *auditory nerves* receiving sensory axons from the

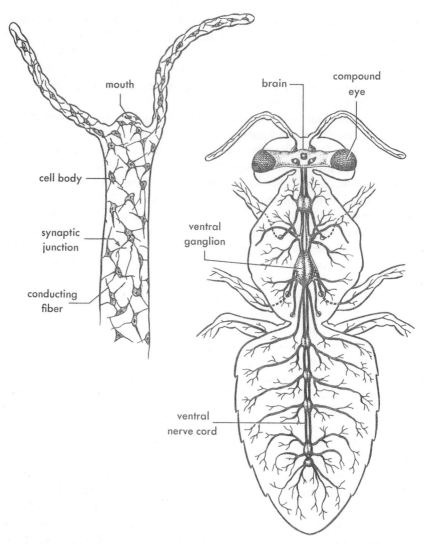

Fig. 10-2. The basic structure of nervous systems in a simple and a complex invertebrate animal. Note that even the diffuse nerve net (left) of the hydra (Phylum Coelenterata) is made up of distinct neurons with synapses at their points of contact. The diagram of an insect nervous system (right) shows the large ganglia and nerve trunks that are made up of thousands of neurons. (Modified from R. E. Snodgrass, *Anatomy of the Honeybee.* Ithaca, N. Y., Comstock Press, 1956.)

ears and also from the *inner ear labyrinth,* which is sensitive to accelerations imparted to the body. The tenth cranial nerves, called the *vagus nerves,* send branches to the larynx, the lungs, the heart, and the digestive tract.

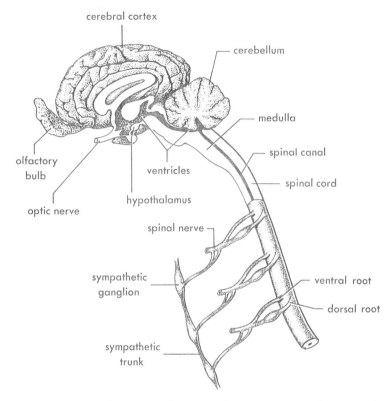

Fig. 10-3. General structure of the central nervous system of a mammal. Note that the paired spinal nerves emerge from the spinal cord as dorsal and ventral roots, which join and are connected to the sympathetic ganglia. The dorsal roots contain sensory neurons; the ventral roots consist mainly of motor neurons carrying impulses away from the spinal cord.

The brain displays enlargements concerned primarily with definite types of regulatory function. Dorsal to the *medulla*, the posterior portion of the brain, and just anterior to the spinal cord is the *cerebellum,* which is concerned with posture and balance. It is small in fishes and amphibians, progressively larger and convoluted in reptiles, birds, and mammals. The medulla itself contains areas concerned with hearing, and control of respiration and circulation, among other functions. At the opposite end of the brain are *olfactory lobes* concerned with reactions to odors, and in mammals especially this anterior portion is greatly enlarged into the *cerebral cortex* where the most complex regulatory behavior is organized. In between are many specialized areas of which one of the most important is the *hypothalamus,* portions of which regulate food and water intake, body temperature in birds and mammals, and some aspects of reproductive behavior. More important than the subdivisions of the brain of any animal, however, is the basic nature of the cellular structures and processes that occur within them, and it is to these that we can now turn our attention.

THE FUNCTIONING OF NERVE CELLS

Along all axons travel *nerve impulses,* the basic "messages" that regulate the actions of other cells at their terminations. In all types of axons the nerve impulses are basically the same, differing only in minor details. They travel rapidly, although not nearly so fast as electric currents, light waves, or even sound waves. Large axons transmit impulses faster than small ones, and their rate of travel increases with temperature. In mammalian axons the rate varies from about 1 to 100 meters per second. The impulse itself is a transient set of biochemical reactions occurring mainly at the cell membrane of the axon, and accompanied by a small and very brief change in electrical potential, known as the *action potential.* Although the metabolic rate increases during and after passage of an impulse, the action potential is the most easily measured sign that a nerve impulse is occurring. The cell membrane of an inactive axon, like those of most other cells, has a slight accumulation of positively charged potassium ions at its outer surface; hence the outside of the axon is electrically positive relative to the cytoplasm. When an impulse passes a given part of the axon, the cell membrane suddenly becomes much more permeable to positively charged ions than when it is at rest. Sodium ions then diffuse inward, and potassium outward during the very small fraction of a second before the membrane recovers its resting properties and by means of active transport restores the previous distribution of the Na^+ and K^+ ions. The movement of these ions produces in turn the action potential, which is a brief change of potential in a negative direction when measured by an electrode just outside the axon. The duration of these changes at a given point on an axon is only about one millisecond ($\frac{1}{1000}$th second), but because of the speed of impulse conduction the length of axon involved at any one time is a few millimeters, or hundreds of times its own diameter. (See Fig. 10-4.)

Nerve impulses are discrete, unitary events, and in a given axon they are all alike. By analogy to computing machines, the all-or-nothing nature of the nerve impulse, discovered about fifty years ago by biologists, has been transposed into the language of electrical engineers by describing conduction of impulses along axons as "digital." A given axon varies greatly in the frequency at which nerve impulses are transmitted, from none at all or a few per second up to maximum rates of almost a thousand impulses per second. It is the frequency of impulses that signals the strength of excitation delivered by the axon at its terminal synapse. For example, when motor neurons conduct impulses at a higher frequency, they cause a stronger contraction of

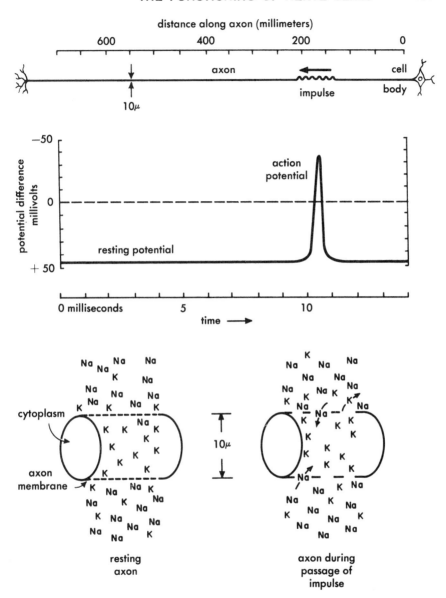

Fig. 10-4. A nerve impulse and its accompanying action potential diagramed approximately to scale. Note that the length of axon surface involved in the impulse at any instant is much greater than the diameter of the axon. The lower part of the figure shows diagrammatically the movement of a small fraction of the K⁺ and Na⁺ ions across the cell membrane during its brief period of enhanced permeability as the impulse passes.

the muscle fibers they serve. Once this frequency has exceeded a few impulses per second, the muscle is excited into a sustained contraction as described in Chapter 6, and the strength of the contraction is roughly proportional to the frequency of impulses in the motor nerve. Likewise, strong excitation of a sense organ causes a higher frequency of impulses in the axons of its sensory nerve. A general principle that applies to all parts of all nervous systems is this: *whenever an axon conducts impulses at a higher frequency it is signaling a higher level of excitation,* and the synapse at which it ends is influenced more strongly. This principle, long known to biologists, has also been glamorized recently by translation into the language of engineering as "the frequency modulation of axonal conduction."

Axons, however, are only one element of nerve cells, and all axons end at synapses. When a nerve impulse arrives at a synapse, it may or may not initiate another impulse in the cell with which it comes into such close proximity; only a minority of impulses reaching synapses produce corresponding impulses in another cell. Since most axons branch, especially those within the central nervous system, and since an impulse spreads into all branches, the number of impulses present at any given moment will obviously increase indefinitely unless they disappear somewhere. It is at synapses that the majority do disappear. Synapses are thus places where nerve impulses may or may not proceed from one cell to another. They are control points, places of decision where it is determined whether a given event is to produce a particular set of consequences within the animal's body. A nerve impulse can travel in both directions along an axon, although normally it is initiated at the dendrites or cell body and thus has only one direction open. At all synapses (with a few exceptions, including those in the nerve nets of coelenterates) conduction is in one direction only, from what are called for convenience the *presynaptic* axonal endings to either the dendrites or cell body of the *postsynaptic* cell. (See Fig. 10-5.)

Since both the endings of axons and dendrites are highly branched in most cases, a given axon usually leads to synapses on several other cells, and any neuron in the central nervous system receives axonal endings from a number of what for it are presynaptic neurons. In a human brain or that of any other large mammal there are more than 10^{10} neurons—more cells than there are people inhabiting the earth. Since each one has synaptic connections with many others, the number of possible connections between cells in any nervous system is astronomical.

SUMMATION AND INHIBITION

What then determines whether a given impulse crosses the synapse at which it arrives? Two important factors are known, *summation* and *inhibition,* and their interplay is believed to account for much of the functioning of nervous systems. Two or more impulses arriving at a given synapse are more likely than one to initiate another impulse in the cell across the synaptic gap. They may arrive over the same axon within a small frac-

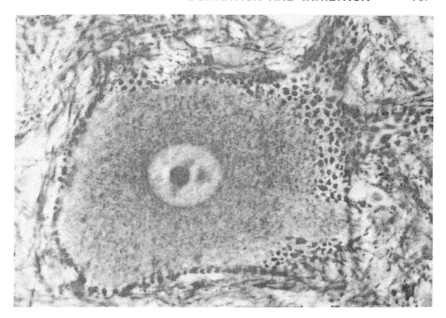

Fig. 10-5. Photomicrograph of the cell body of a motor neuron with many synapses on its surface. Short lengths of the presynaptic axons are stained black. This cell was activated by several presynaptic axons, each of which had a large number of terminal branches. (From G. L. Rasmussen, *New Research Techniques of Neuroanatomy*, 1959. Courtesy of the author and Charles C. Thomas, Publisher.)

tion of a second, in which case the phenomenon is called *temporal summation,* or they may reach the synapses on a given cell over two or more different axons, in which case the process is called *spatial summation.* A common type of temporal summation is observed when a sensory axon entering the spinal cord sends impulses at different frequencies to a synapse on a motor neuron activating a muscle of the leg. This pattern of neurons underlies many reflexes such as the knee jerk, in which a sudden mechanical stretching of sense organs in the tendon at the knee may elicit a sharp contraction of the extensor muscles of the leg. If the impulse frequency in the sensory neuron leading from one of these sense organs to a synapse in the spinal cord is below a critical level, no impulse is produced in the motor nerve; if it increases above this value, one or more impulses do travel out to the muscle. (See Fig. 10-6.) Spatial summation often occurs at the same type of synapse when nerve impulses reach it over several sensory axons within a fraction of a second. Temporal and spatial summation are essential for all transmission of impulses across synapses in the central nervous systems.

Nerve impulses converging on a given synapse often produce just the opposite effect to summation—that is, one set of impulses may offset the effects of another—and this phenomenon is called *inhibition.* At a particular synapse such as one of those involved in the knee jerk, impulses may arrive over sensory nerves at a sufficient rate to stimulate a steady series of impulses in the motor nerve. If now certain other neurons in the spinal cord are activated and begin to send impulses over their axons to the same synapse, fewer impulses will occur in the motor neuron, or none at all. The higher the impulse frequency in this inhibitory nerve, the less will be the transmission across the synapse. Most cell bodies of neurons or their dendrites receive many synaptic endings where axons of other neurons can either excite or inhibit. Hence each neuron is always subject to both excitatory and inhibitory influence. It is the balance between these two influences that determines whether the cell in question will itself be stimulated to convey nerve impulses along its own axon.

As far as we know, a given axonal ending is either excitatory or inhibitory, but this is a property of the ending, not of the postsynaptic cell body. It is probable that many axons branch and lead to inhibitory endings at some synapses and excitatory endings at others.

THE MOLECULAR BASIS OF SYNAPTIC CONDUCTION

Important information about synaptic conduction has also been gathered by measuring *synaptic potentials* by means of a very small electrode placed close to a synapse while it is receiving impulses over excitatory and inhibitory axons. Synaptic potentials resemble the action potentials of an axon in some respects but are very different in others. They usually have the same polarity; that is, the arrival of excitatory impulses causes the electrode to become more negative. A synaptic potential lasts somewhat longer than the action potential—several milliseconds instead of one or a very few milliseconds. The major difference between the two is that synaptic potentials are variable in magnitude; at a given synapse they can be small or large. A low frequency of arriving impulses generates only small synaptic potentials and no action potential at all. As the frequency of arriving impulses increases, the synaptic potential grows gradually until it reaches a critical value and an all-or-nothing impulse is suddenly generated in the postsynaptic cell. (See Fig. 10-6.) The arrival of inhibitory impulses sometimes has just the opposite effect—that is, to reduce the synaptic potential. Both excitatory and inhibitory impulses are alike in being all-or-nothing events, and both have action potentials of the same kind. The fact that electrically identical impulses arriving over inhibitory and excitatory axons cause opposite effects at the synapse proves that something more is involved than a simple electrical process whereby the negative action potential at one cell membrane produces a similar negativity at the other and thus initiates a new nerve impulse.

The same type of interplay between excitatory and inhibitory axons

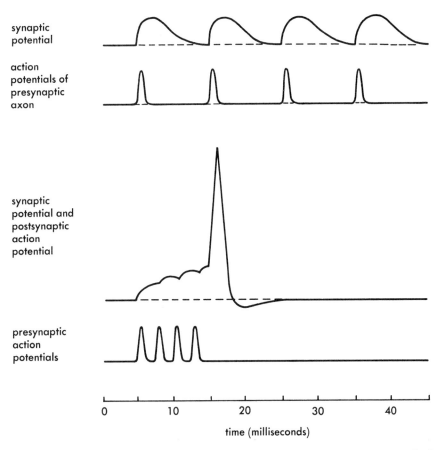

synaptic
potential

action
potentials of
presynaptic
axon

synaptic
potential and
postsynaptic
action
potential

presynaptic
action
potentials

0   10   20   30   40

time (milliseconds)

Fig. 10-6. Diagrammatic representation of electrical events that accompany arrival of nerve impulses at a synapse. The action potentials of a presynaptic axon are shown as simple spikes; they have a higher frequency in the lower record than in the upper one. Immediately above the presynaptic action potentials are shown the synaptic potentials as they might be measured by a microelectrode very close to the synapse. In the upper record there is one synaptic potential for each arriving nerve impulse. But at a higher frequency of arriving impulses *temporal summation* takes place and an action potential is set up in the postsynaptic neruon. This new action potential appears larger because the electrode is in a more favorable location to pick it up along with the synaptic potential. At most synapses there would also be inhibitory endings that would tend to offset the effects of excitatory impulses such as those shown in this figure.

occurs at the neuromuscular junctions of many muscles, including cardiac muscle of vertebrates and skeletal muscle of the Crustacea, but not the skeletal muscle of vertebrates. Although the hearts of vertebrates beat spontaneously even when isolated from the rest of the animal, they are normally regulated by two sets of nerves. *Sympathetic nerves* arising in certain of the sympathetic ganglia carry impulses that accelerate the rate at which the heart beats, and branches of the *vagus* (tenth cranial) *nerve* convey impulses that cause a slowing of the heart or actually stop it altogether if the impulse frequency is sufficiently high in a sufficient number of vagus axons.

The muscles that move the appendages of crustaceans such as the lobster receive a similar type of double innervation: one set of axons causes the muscles to contract, and another tends to cause relaxation. In vertebrate skeletal muscle, inhibition occurs not at the neuromuscular junctions but at synapses in the spinal cord. Similar principles are believed to govern all cases in which excitation and inhibition interact at synapses, but the molecular basis of the competition is most clearly established for vetebrate cardiac muscle, where it was also first successfully analyzed.

The major clue to the situation was the discovery that the blood flowing out of a heart that had just been slowed by strong vagus stimulation contained a substance that would exert an identical inhibitory effect on another heart into which the blood was experimentally conducted. The substance is *acetyl choline,* which has also been found to be released in minute but effective amounts at many other types of synapses. (Acetyl choline is ordinarily destroyed rather rapidly by a special enzyme present in blood and most tissues, and thus its presence after vagus stimulation is demonstrable only after this enzyme has been poisoned by an appropriate drug.) After acceleration of the heart by similar stimulation of its sympathetic nerve supply, another substance, *adrenalin,* is liberated. Both acetyl choline and adrenalin can be added in minute quantities to cardiac muscle, or to whole hearts, and they produce the same effect as stimulation of vagus or sympathetic nerves respectively.

A very common type of control mechanism comprises such opposed nerve supplies, each of which produces at its axonal endings very low concentrations of a highly active substance that mediates the excitatory or inhibitory effect. In many cases, however, the particular substances have not yet been identified. In vertebrate animals many organs receive a dual nerve supply very similar to that which regulates the heart. The many sympathetic nerve trunks that ramify from the chain of sympathetic ganglia produce adrenalin or a similar molecule at their axonal endings. The vagus nerve together with branches from spinal nerves in the posterior portion of the body contribute a widespread network of axons that liberate acetyl choline at their endings. This network is called the *parasympathetic nervous system,* and the two systems together make up what is called the *autonomic nervous system* of vertebrate animals. (See Fig. 10-3.) Their general effects can be summarized in a few significant generalizations.

The sympathetic nerves, most of which emerge from the sympathetic ganglia shown in Fig. 10-3, prepare the animal for vigorous action. The heart beat is accelerated, and arterioles in the digestive tract are constricted while those in skeletal muscle are caused to dilate, with the result that blood is distributed to those muscles most likely to be activated. Sympathetic nerves have an inhibitory effect, however, on the smooth muscles of the intestine (except for those of sphincters that close off one part of the digestive tract from another), and this is in keeping with the general preparation of the animal for action rather than digestion of food. The parasympathetic system has opposite effects, in general, causing dilation of capillaries in the digestive tract, activating smooth muscles there, and tending to relax sphincter muscles. Many other parts of the sympathetic and parasympathetic systems have opposed effects that are understandable on this basis.

The antagonistic actions of sympathetic and parasympathetic systems maintain a balance throughout the whole animal; this balance is analogous to the regulated firmness of an animal's leg that results from partial contraction of opposed skeletal muscles. Neither member of the pair predominates totally except under the most unusual conditions, and their graded interplay is typical of the general strategy of control by a balance of opposed mechanisms that is widely utilized in all highly organized animals. It is also significant that adrenalin is produced not only at the endings of sympathetic nerves but also in each of a pair of specialized glands that liberate it directly into the blood. This gland is the *medulla* or central portion of the *adrenal gland,* so named because it lies close to the kidneys. It is stimulated by its own sympathetic nerve supply, from an adjacent sympathetic ganglion. The adrenalin distributed generally by the circulatory system acts on much the same organs as that produced by sympathetic nerve endings in them, but there is apparently an advantage in having this alternate means of widespread and relatively massive distribution of the chemical messenger that alerts the animal's many tissues for vigorous activity.

Substances such as adrenalin and acetyl choline are called *neurohumors,* meaning that they are produced by nerve cells and stimulate or inhibit other cells. At most synapses the target cell is only a few hundred Å distant, but in the case of the adrenal gland it may be at the opposite end of the animal's body. The electron microscope has even revealed hollow vesicles roughly 500 Å in diameter in the cytoplasm of presynaptic cells close to the synapse. These may contain the neurohumor, but their minute size has so far prevented a positive identification. Biologists are discovering close associations between systems of nervous and hormonal control in more and more cases, and this leads us naturally to a consideration of endocrine glands that produce hormones as their principal function.

ENDOCRINE CONTROL SYSTEMS

The medulla of the adrenal gland is one of a number of endocrine glands, so named because they discharge their products into the blood stream rather than into ducts leading to the outside surface or into the digestive tract. The function of the hormones thus secreted is to affect in some way a target organ or tissue remote from the endocrine gland concerned. Thus acetyl choline is considered a neurohumor but not a hormone, whereas adrenalin is both. In all cases a given hormone is present in the blood only in very minute, usually undetectable, quantities. A hormone meets the following criteria: (1) it is produced in a particular endocrine gland, (2) removal of the gland causes the failure of some other organ to develop or function normally, and (3) in the absence of the endocrine gland, artificial replacement of the hormone in the body restores the target organ to its normal size and functional capacity.

Several hormones have very general effects throughout the body. These include several from the *cortex* of the adrenal glands that regulate ionic balance, carbohydrate metabolism, and, in other ways not clearly understood, promote the general vigor of the animal. The *thyroid* gland, located close to the larynx, produces *thyroxin,* which increases the general metabolic rate and which is also essential for the metamorphosis of amphibian tadpoles into adult frogs or toads. Endocrine cells located in the pancreas (a gland containing other cells that secrete digestive enzymes into the intestine) produce *insulin,* which is necessary for the utilization of glucose by cells throughout the body and for its removal from the blood stream. Very little is known of how these hormone molecules produce their observed effects.

Another group of hormones is produced by the anterior portion of the *pituitary gland,* located just ventral to the hypothalamus. These are protein hormones that stimulate the growth and functional development of other tissues. One, the *growth hormone,* is essential for general growth of a young animal, especially the long bones of its skeleton. Two others, the *adrenocorticotropic hormone* (ACTH) and the *thyrotropic hormone,* stimulate the adrenal cortex and the thyroid gland respectively to produce their own hormones. The best known hormones of the anterior pituitary are the *gonadotropic* hormones that cause the gonads to develop and begin to produce ova or sperm. The posterior part of the pituitary gland is supplied by neurons from the hypothalamus, and among other hormones the posterior pituitary of mammals contains, during the late stages of pregnancy, *oxytocin,* which causes the muscles of the uterus to contract rhythmically. Oxytocin is a polypeptide and is one of the few pituitary hormones whose chemical structure is definitely known; its structure, however, gives no clue to the reasons for its specific action on smooth muscle in the uterus. Finally, the gonads themselves produce *sex hormones: testosterone* from the interstitial cells of the testis and *estrogen* from cells in the ovary that are located close to the ova during their formation.

This does not complete the list of vertebrate hormones, any more than other organ systems have been described completely in this brief and elementary book. The relationship between anterior pituitary and ovaries will be considered briefly, however, because it illustrates an important general principle of endocrine control. The sex hormones stimulate the growth of the secondary sexual characters—the mammary glands, external genitalia, hair near the genital openings, and those structures and colored parts of animals that are different in the two sexes, such as the antlers of deer, and the combs of roosters. The gonadotropic hormones of the anterior pituitary not only stimulate the growth of the cells in the gonads that produce ova or sperm, they also lead to the functional development of the interstitial cells that produce the sex hormones.

The sex hormones have an important effect in addition to the stimulation of the secondary sexual characters. When they are carried in the blood to the anterior pituitary they specifically inhibit the production of gonadotropic hormones, thus reducing the original stimulus to the cells that produced them. In this way another type of balance is achieved between two related but opposed control systems. In females, the result is usually a cycle of reproductive activity; in males, a balance preventing inadequate or excessive development of the testes and secondary sexual characters. Other endocrine mechanisms also operate in balance to prepare the uterus of a female mammal for its special role in pregnancy.

The hormone oxytocin mentioned above is found in the posterior pituitary gland, although it is produced in certain neurons of the hypothalamus; from its origin in these specialized cell bodies it travels slowly along their axons to be stored in the posterior pituitary. This is but one example of another important aspect of animal control systems known as *neurosecretion*—that is, the production by neurons of particular molecules such as acetyl choline, adrenalin, or oxytocin that have specific effects on other cells. Neurosecretion may be as widespread and important a function of neurons as their better known role in the conduction of nerve impulses along axons and their screening at synapses. Nerve impulses serve for the rapid conveying of specific quantitative excitation to particular cells, including both positive excitation and negative inhibition. Neurohumors seem from what little is known of them, to be concerned with qualitative effects, preparing the animal for a particular kind of activity—vigorous exercise in the case of adrenalin, reproduction in the case of gonadotropic hormones.

THE ORIGIN OF NERVOUS EXCITATION

It is appropriate at this point to inquire where all the activity of the nervous system originates. Many of the nerve impulses arise in sense organs and flow into the central nervous system along the sensory nerves. The major types of *receptor cells* are important because they are the only channels of information between the outside world and the central nervous system. Many receptors are concentrated into elaborate sense organs such as the eye or ear, but roughly as many others are distributed widely throughout all tissues of the animal's body. The simplest are undifferentiated nerve endings that are common in the skin and sensitive to mechanical deformation, temperature changes, and relatively pronounced changes in their chemical environment. The more vigorous such stimuli are, the higher the frequency of nerve impulses that travel along these neurons to the brain. In ourselves and presumably in other animals many of these impulses produce sensations of pain when sufficient numbers of neurons carry impulses at high frequencies. Increased sensitivity to minute amounts of energy of specific types is attained by specialized receptor cells, and when they are organized into sense organs the resulting sensitivity sometimes approaches limits set by the physical nature of the stimulus energy.

Many fishes have sensitive receptors lining an olfactory pit, located on the head, through which water circulates as the fish swims about. In some cases the fish recognizes a particular odor at such a low concentration that only one or a very few molecules can reach any one receptor cell.

In the ears and related sense organs of vertebrate animals very small oscillatory pressure changes that constitute sound waves in the surrounding air or water are conducted to specialized *hair cells*. From these project hairs that resemble cilia except that they do not move spontaneously. These hairs are usually in contact with a small mass of material called an *otolith* which has a different density from the rest of the tissues, and as a result sound waves reaching the hair cell move it slightly more or less than the otolith and deform the cell surface ever so slightly where the hair emerges. So sensitive are these auditory receptors in both terrestrial vertebrates and many fishes that airborne or underwater sounds can be heard when the hair cell moves by as little as 10^{-11} centimeter, a distance only about one hundredth the diameter of a hydrogen atom. Of course the atoms and molecules making up these receptor cells are vastly larger than this, and millions of molecules are undergoing oscillatory movements through this small distance many times per second. The sensitivity of ears could not be much increased without the animal beginning to hear the random thermal agitation of the molecules comprising its ear.

Eyes are no less remarkable than ears in this regard. Transparent tissues that grow to have the exact shape required of image-forming lens systems focus an image of the outside world on a *retina* or mosaic of visual receptor cells. In parts of the eyes of many vertebrates these visual receptors are packed within about three microns of each other, so that they can be individually stimulated by fine details of the focused image down to the limits of resolution set by the wave length of visible light. Visual receptors contain a photosensitive pigment called *rhodopsin,* or similar substances; light causes these to undergo chemical reactions that set up nerve impulses in an adjacent neuron. Light consists of discrete "all-or-nothing" units called quanta, and some visual receptors are so sensitive that a single quantum suffices to stimulate them and yield at least one nerve impulse. This sensitivity obviously cannot be improved upon.

High sensitivity is only one way in which receptor cells and their sensory neurons are specialized to provide useful information to the central nervous system. The customary interplay of excitation and inhibition occurs not only at synapses in the brain where sensory axons have their endings, but also in the sense organs themselves—especially in the retina of a vertebrate animal, which contains both receptors and a whole network of neurons and synapses through which impulses must pass before reaching the optic nerve. Stimulation of one visual receptor often elicits impulses that tend to inhibit synapses receiving impulses from adjacent ones. This competition between impulses arriving over axons from neighboring receptors heightens the discriminations that the retina can make between fine gradations of light and shade.

Limitations of space compel us to stop here, as we have done elsewhere, just when the story is becoming most exciting, with the hope that readers will be interested enough to pursue the subject in more advanced reading or study.

THE ESSENCE OF A LIVING ANIMAL

Sense organs are not the only sources of nerve impulses for the central nervous system. Many of its cells also exhibit *spontaneous activity*, sending impulses down their axons even when isolated from all outside stimulation. There is thus no dearth of excitation within a brain; the question is, how does it all add up to a system that controls the animal's activities in an appropriately coordinated fashion? Of all the organ systems the central nervous system contributes the most to making an animal the uniquely organized entity it is. Yet when we view this organ under the microscope we see an endlessly tangled forest where the cell bodies of neurons, their branching axons, dendrites, and glial cells are intermingled like a thicket of tree trunks, branches, and vines in what appears to be utter confusion. (See Fig. 10-7.) Out of seeming chaos comes orderly regulation and control of all the varied and versatile organs of the animal's body.

Any part of any central nervous system differs from other organs in that each individual cell tends to have a specific function that is often quite different from that of its immediate neighbor. Adjacent muscle fibers all contract in nearly the same way, but one of two adjacent neurons may excite a particular synapse, while the other causes inhibition. In an area of the brain where axons from the retina converge, one cell may respond when a light is turned on, and another when it goes off, and a third may ignore a light that flickers on and off but respond with a barrage of impulses when a spot of light moves over the surface of the retina. Furthermore, among the millions of neurons in a brain there is not only a tremendous division of labor but also a great duplication and overlap of function, so that many may be destroyed without appreciable damage to the effectiveness of the whole, organized brain.

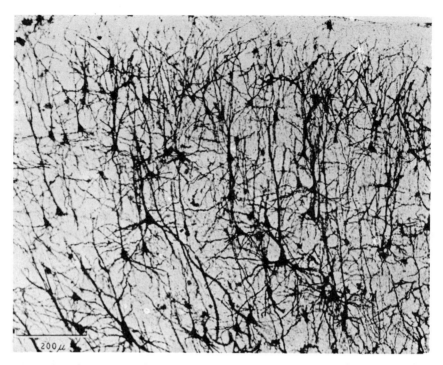

Fig. 10-7. Photomicrograph of a typical portion of the cerebral cortex of a mammal. A few cell bodies are visible, and their axons are thicker than the myriad of other axons and dendrites that interlace across the field of the microscope. In such preparations only a fraction of the neurons actually present are made visible by the stains employed, and none of the glial cells are visible. Synapses may occur at any of the points of contact between axons, dendrites, and cell bodies. Even in this tiny piece of brain tissue one can scarcely estimate the number of possible routes over which nerve impulses might travel. (From D. A. Sholl, *The Organization of the Cerebral Cortex.* 1956. Courtesy of Methuen and Co., Publishers.)

In studying the workings of brains, biologists have hardly succeeded yet in seeing the forest for the trees. The attempt to do so, however, is being actively pursued on many fronts—from highly detailed studies of the submicroscopic structure and biochemistry of the synaptic membranes where such decisive events take place, to attempts to analyze the behavior of whole animals and achieve some orderly understanding of the factors that control what they do with the bodily machinery at their disposal. At this stage in the history of science no one can explain how a brain really works, not even the nerve net of a coelenterate. This chapter has outlined what contemporary biologists believe are the most significant questions we can ask about nervous systems. With these in mind one can proceed with some perspective to study animals and their behavior in more detail, or await with informed interest the future advances in our knowledge about this and other frontiers of biological thought.

SUGGESTED READING LIST

BEKESY, G. VON, "The ear," *Scientific American,* Aug. 1957, p. 66.

BRAZIER, M. A. B., 1960. *The electrical activity of the nervous system.* New York: 1960. Macmillan.

DAVSON, H., 1959. *A textbook of general physiology,* 2d ed. London: Churchill. Chapters 15-17.

ECCLES, J. C., "The physiology of imagination," *Scientific American,* Sept. 1958, p. 135.

FRENCH, J. D., "The reticular formation," *Scientific American,* May 1957, p. 54.

FUNKENSTEIN, D. H., "The physiology of fear and anger," *Scientific American,* May 1955, p. 74.

GERARD, R. W., "The dynamics of inhibition," *Scientific American,* Sept. 1948, p. 44.

———, "What is memory?," *Scientific American,* Sept. 1953, p. 118.

GRAY, WALTER W., "The electrical activity of the brain," *Scientific American,* June 1954, p. 54.

———, "The great ravelled knot," *Scientific American,* Oct. 1948, p. 26.

HESS, E. H., " 'Imprinting' in animals," *Scientific American,* March 1958, p. 81.

KATZ, B., "The nerve impulse," *Scientific American,* Nov. 1952, p. 55.

KEYNES, R. D., "The nerve impulse and the squid," *Scientific American,* Dec. 1958, p. 83.

LI, C. H., "The pituitary," *Scientific American,* Oct. 1950, p. 18.

LORENZ, K., "The evolution of behavior," *Scientific American,* Dec. 1958, p. 67.

MAGOUN, H. W., 1958. *The waking brain.* Springfield, Ill.: Thomas.

PROSSER, C. L., and BROWN, F. A., Jr, 1961. *Comparative animal physiology,* 2d ed. Philadelphia: Saunders.

ROWLAND, U., "Conditioning and brain waves," *Scientific American,* Aug. 1959, p. 89.

SPERRY, R. W., "The eye and the brain," *Scientific American,* May 1956, p. 48.

THORPE, W. H., 1956. *Learning and instinct in animals.* Cambridge, Mass.: Harvard University Press.

TURNER, C. D., 1961. *General endocrinology,* 3d ed. Philadelphia: Saunders.

WALD, G., "Eye and camera," *Scientific American,* Aug. 1950, p. 32.

WARDEN, C. J., "Animal intelligence," *Scientific American,* June 1951, p. 64.

WILLIAMS, C. M., "The juvenile hormone," *Scientific American,* Feb. 1958, p. 67.

YOUNG, J. Z., 1957. *The life of mammals.* New York: Oxford University Press. Chapters 17-33.

INDEX